# ELECTRONIC TEST EQUIPMENT

# ELECTRONIC TEST EQUIPMENT

**by Harry T. Kitchen**

**Fountain Press**
**Argus Books Limited**
Station Road, Kings Langley,
Herts, England

Consultant Editor: Norman Stevens

Fountain Press
Argus Books Limited
Station Road, Kings Langley,
Herts, England

First Published 1975
© Harry T. Kitchen 1975

ISBN  0  85242  427  2

Typeset and printed
in Great Britain by
REDWOOD BURN LIMITED
Trowbridge & Esher

# CONTENTS

# PREFACE

ALL BRANCHES OF ENGINEERING require measuring instruments, but nowhere is the field so diverse or so complex as in electronics. This book is intended to help the student, the hobby enthusiast, the newcomer to electronics and the practising engineer who feels that a little revision would not come amiss, not forgetting the specialist engineer who wishes to extend his general knowledge of electronic test equipment. A re-examination of principles can be very reward-ing—even chastening!—and it is no new experience to discover just how much one has forgotten, or never quite got the hang of in the first place.

When writing this book, I found it very difficult to contain my own enthusiasm and as a result the dividing line between theory and practice may be found by some readers to wander a little, so that some subjects or aspects have been overstated at the expense of others. This is to a degree inevitable, as we don't all think alike, and I hope that the reader who disagrees with me will do so kindly.

An often difficult problem is selecting a particular instrument for any given task. For the amateur or the impecunious professional, the acquisition of instruments can form a very large portion of his budget and an injudicious purchase can be worse than the proverbial millstone. The advice offered and the suggestions made, in this book are necessarily personal, but are based on many years in and around the field of electronics.

Of the circuits illustrated, some are shown in greater detail than others as I felt that these had definite practical applications. The commercial circuits are included, sometimes to make a point, sometimes as a matter of technical interest. I feel sure than I am not the only one who is inquisitive about the technical expertise that is hidden behind those sleek exteriors. The circuits are, of course, the copyright of the manufacturers concerned.

Some of the photographs used for illustrations have been taken by myself, while the remainder have been kindly supplied by the

vii

manufacturers, who have also supplied the circuit diagrams. Without their co-operation, this book would have been that much less interesting and for that reason I would like to express my appreciation to them.

My thanks are particularly due to Advance Electronics Ltd for the loan of two of their delightful oscilloscopes, the OS250 and the OS1000A, without the use of which some of the most interesting and useful waveforms could not have been made.

I would also like to thank the editors of *Practical Electronics*, *Practical Wireless* and *Radio Constructor* for permission to reproduce photographs and brief details of test instruments that I had the pleasure of constructing and which were published as constructional articles in their magazines.

*Bulkington, Warks, 1975*                              *Harry T. Kitchen*

CHAPTER ONE

# VOLTAGE, CURRENT AND RESISTANCE MEASUREMENTS

MEASURING INSTRUMENTS of the 'meter' variety are, with one exception, dependent for their operation on the fact that a magnetic field surrounds every conductor through which a current is passing, as well as on the fact that the strength of the field is proportional to the current. The exception is the electrostatic meter, to be considered later. The most common way of utilising this effect is to cause the field so produced to react with another field. This is what is done in the case of the moving coil meter—known as the D'Arsonval meter in American publications—and in the case of Dynamometers. The different types of meters can now be considered a little more closely.

## The Moving Coil Meter

The essentials of this are shown in Fig. 1.1. This consists of a magnet, specially 'horse shoe' shaped so that it can be more easily incorporated in the barrel of a complete meter movement. The magnetic field is concentrated in the air-gap between the two pole pieces of the horse shoe magnet by a soft iron core, which also tends to provide a more uniform and radial magnetic field in which the moving coil can operate.

The moving coil itself consists of very many turns of very fine wire, wound on an aluminium former, and suspended on jewelled bearings. Current to the coil is carried on a pair of oppositely wound control springs, which must be insulated from each other and from the frame of the meter.

When the meter is not passing current, the point at which the two springs cancel each other is arranged to coincide with the required 'zero' setting. The balance of these springs can be upset not only with the passing of time, but by mechanical shock, extreme temperatures, and the like. It is therefore necessary to provide an

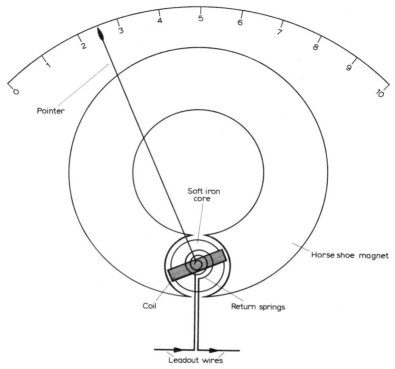

Fig. 1.1 Basic moving coil movement.

external zero adjustment by means of a small screw that lies flush from the front of the meter.

The sensitivity of the meter, i.e. the amount the coil moves for any given current, is dependent on the strength of the magnetic field, and also on the number of turns of wire comprising the coil. Another factor affecting sensitivity is the air gap in which the coil operates; the smaller the gap, the higher the sensitivity, all other factors being equal. It is interesting to note here that British Physical Laboratories, one of Britain's leading meter manufacturers, have reduced the size of their meter barrels considerably, as well as lightening the entire meter movement, by the use of high **BH** value magnets made of Hycomax or Ticonal 1300.

As the torque is dependent on the current flowing through the coil, the pointer movements should be linear, and the scale calibrated in equal increments. In practice, some non-linearity is inevitable, although in a well designed movement it should be reduced to negligible proportions.

The spindle carrying the coil and pointer is subjected to four forces: an actuating force, a restoring force, a damping force, and a restrictive force. The actuating force, in the case of a moving coil meter, is due to the current flowing through the coil, the magnetic field of which reacts with the magnetic field of the permanent magnet. The restoring force is provided by the control springs which return the pointer to zero when the actuating force is removed. The damping force operates against the actuating force, compelling the pointer to assume its indicating position of rest without excessive oscillation to and fro. Damping may be accomplished electrically or mechanically; in the case of moving coil instruments, it is almost invariably electrical.

**Damping Force**

Having looked at the actuating force, we can now look at the damping force. Electrical damping in a meter is achieved by winding the coil on a former made of aluminium. When the coil begins to rotate, a voltage is induced in the former, due to its cutting the lines of force produced by the magnet. This induced voltage causes eddy currents in the former, which in turn produce a magnetic field in opposition to that of the permanent magnet. The braking action so caused, quickly brings the pointer to its position of rest without undue oscillations, but has not, it must be noted, any effect on its final resting position on the scale.

The restrictive force, which may cause the pointer to stick or jerk, is due to the pivots, and may be due to faulty design—very rare—or more commonly to damage or to fluff, dust, and grit. In all high grade instruments, sticking or jerking due to the pivots is reduced to negligible proportions by the use of hardened and highly polished conical pivots bearing in jewelled supports. The ingress of dust and other harmful substances is reduced by the use of close fitting cases surrounding the meter movement.

If the current passing through the coil varies too rapidly, the deflection will be proportional to the average current. If an alternating current is passed through the coil the meter will indicate zero. A moment's thought will show why this should be so. Let us suppose that the positive half of an a.c. is passing through the coil. The coil will try to move, but will be impeded by its own inertia, inertia being the opposition a body at rest offers to any force trying to move it, and to a lesser extent by its damping. Before the coil can move very far, if it moves at all, the polarity of the a.c. will have changed, and will now be trying to move it in the opposite direction. The pointer will be seen to tremble at the frequency of the a.c., provided that this is low enough to actuate the coil. A moving coil meter, therefore, responds only to d.c.

## Sensitivities

Moving coil meters are available with varying sensitivities, and are specified according to the current required for full scale deflection, commonly abbreviated to f.s.d. The most sensitive meters in *general* use require 50μA for f.s.d. At the other end of the scale, the most commonly used meters have f.s.d. figures in tens of Amps, though special purpose meters measure much higher currents.

The internal resistance of a moving coil meter is often required to be known, when, for example, current multiplying resistors must be calculated. This is a function of the gauge of wire used, and of its length. The requirements of high sensitivity can be met, to a degree, by the use of a more powerful magnet. At the same time, or possibly as an alternative, the coil can be wound with more turns of wire, so providing a more powerful field for a given current. This may then conflict with the requirements of low mass of the coil assembly, and so a smaller gauge of wire must be used. Coil resistances are generally printed on the meter dial or barrel, or can be ascertained from the manufacturer, or can be measured. Tolerances are generally to ±10%.

The *voltage* necessary to provide f.s.d. is sometimes of interest, and can be calculated by simple Ohm's Law by multiplying meter f.s.d. current by meter coil resistance. Matters are sometimes arranged so that the voltage necessary for f.s.d. is 75mV.

## Taut Band Suspension

Moving coil meters of high sensitivity are more susceptible to damage due to shock and vibration than are less sensitive meters, although modern meters are far superior in this respect than were those of yesteryear. Suspensions by taut band are popular as a means of combating damage, although here it is interesting to learn that BPL have come to the conclusion that for f.s.d.'s above 50μA, pivoted bearings are best, providing the correct pivot point radius and bearing radius and spring strength of the sprung bearing jewels are selected, and an adequate value of torque to weight ratio is achieved. Below 50μA they state that taut band suspensions must be used.

Taut band suspensions are free from 'stiction' effects, whereby the pointer moves in small, finite jerks, rather than continuously, and from the effects of 'hysteresis' which is the difference in reading obtained between rising and falling currents, when in actual fact the readings should be identical.

## Electrostatic Meters

The electrostatic meter, unlike the moving coil meter just considered, which is current operated, is a true voltmeter. On d.c. voltage, it draws no current as its input resistance is virtually infinite. On a.c. voltage, capacitive effects cause a small current to be drawn, and this is a limiting factor at the higher frequencies.

The principle of this meter is the electrostatic attraction which exists between oppositely charged plates in close proximity. Increased sensitivity is obtained by using two sets of interleaved plates, very carefully insulated from each other and from the frame. The construction, as Fig. 1.2 shows, is not unlike a very highly refined, and delicately constructed, tuning capacitor. One set of plates, the stator, is rigidly fixed, whilst the other set, the rotor, is carefully balanced and rides in jewelled pivots. The pointer is attached to the rotor.

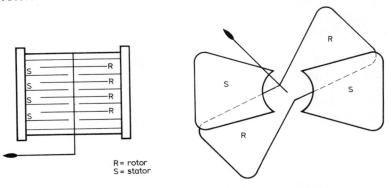

R = rotor
S = stator

Fig. 1.2   Electrostatic voltmeter.

The f.s.d. can be as low as 100 volts, or as high as 100kV, although a more common figure, particularly in television work, is 30kV. The scale should, in theory at least, be linear, but in practice is usually cramped, sometimes at both ends, more usually at the bottom end.

The analogy between a tuning capacitor is a very apt one, for as the plates rotate the capacitance between them changes from, possibly, a few pF at zero, to possibly several hundred pF at f.s.d. Under normal conditions, this is of little consequence, but in r.f. work it can introduce errors. Suitably designed, electrostatic meters can be used on a.c. and d.c. voltage, giving accurate readings, and as such can be used as 'transfer' instruments to compare a known a.c. voltage against an unknown d.c. voltage, or vice versa.

## Thermocouple Meters

Thermocouple meters consist of sensitive moving coil meters connected across a thermocouple, the action of which is as follows: if the junction of two wires made of dissimilar metals is heated, a potential difference is set up across the free ends. This p.d. is proportional to the difference in temperature between the hot junction and the cold ends. Almost any pair of dissimilar metals can be used, but the effect is more pronounced with specific metals. Amongst the metals and alloys commonly used are: nickel, iron, silver, eureka, constantin, chromel, and others.

Thermocouples can be heated in a flame, or by placing them in close proximity to, or touching, a heated body. In this particular application, the thermocouple, in its simplest form, is placed in contact with a wire through which the current to be measured is passed. As the passage of the current heats the wire, so is the thermocouple also heated, producing an e.m.f. which is indicated on the moving coil meter. This, in turn, can be calibrated in terms of current. In practice, the thermocouple is much more sophisticated, for the simple device just described, whilst workable, is not capable of accurate and reproducable results.

Thermocouples are very suitable for radio frequency measurements. Up to several MHz errors are negligible. Above that they increase due to 'skin' effects, but even so can be as low as 5% at 100MHz. As such, they can be used as 'transfer' devices from r.f. to d.c. Since the power in the heater is proportional to the square of the current ($W = I^2R$) the scale will have a square law look about it, i.e. non-linear, with the graduations closing up at the bottom end. Sensitivities as low as 5mA f.s.d. are obtainable, and as such the thermocouple would appear to be a very versatile instrument, which it is. Unfortunately, the thermocouples are relatively fragile, and can be burnt out by an overload as low as 50%.

## Meter Conversions

We have looked at, in turn, moving coil meters, electrostatic meters, and thermocouple meters. All of these have their uses, but by far the most versatile, the most adaptable, meter of all is the moving coil meter. By means of shunt resistors it can measure currents infinitely greater than its own f.s.d.; by means of series resistors it can measure voltages from a few hundreds of millivolts to many thousands of volts; by means of rectifiers it can measure a.c. volts. The list can be extended, of course, but we can make a start on the current shunt resistors for extending the current measuring capability of a simple moving coil meter.

## Extending Current Ranges

To measure *current*, a meter has to be connected in *series* with the supply and the load. If the current to be measured is greater than the f.s.d. rating of the meter, it will be necessary to connect across the meter a shunt resistor. (Aptly named, since it shunts excess current past the meter.) The most common example is the extending of a 1mA meter to measure 10mA, and Fig. 1.3 shows the essentials.

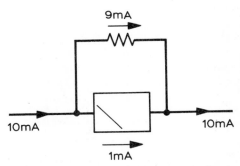

9mA

10mA                                    10mA

1mA

Fig. 1.3    1mA meter, shunted to read 10mA.

The shunt resistor across the meter has a value such that of the *total* load current of 10mA, 9mA flows through the shunt, and only 1mA flows through the meter. It is essential to remember that, though only 1mA is flowing through the meter the actual load current is 10mA, and to multiply by a factor of 10, a feat not requiring great mental strain! If the meter only reads 0·5 for example, the actual current is 0·5 times 10 = 5mA.

**Calculating Current Shunt Resistors**

The selection of a shunt resistor is simple, and can be determined from the formula

$$Rs = \frac{r}{n - I}$$

where Rs is the value of the shunt in ohms, r is the internal resistance of the meter, and n is the current multiplication factor. Thus, if it is required to measure up to 100mA with a 1mA meter, then n = 100, and the term n − 1 = 99. Assuming the meter internal resistance to be 100 ohms, a common value, the shunt will be 100/99 or 1·01 ohms.

An alternative formula which gives the same result is

$$Rs = \frac{Im \text{ times } Rm}{It \text{ minus } Im}$$

where Im is the f.s.d. current of the meter, Rm the meter internal resistance, and It the total current. Substituting the previous figures we get

$$Rs = \frac{I \text{ times } 100}{100 \text{ minus } 1} = \frac{100}{99}$$

or the same answer as before, i.e. 1·01Ω.

Where a single meter is required to provide more than one range extension, individual shunts can be calculated as above. This scheme may be acceptable when readings are required infrequently. If not, changing the shunts can become tiresome; also the shunts can become damaged or lost. In this case, it is wiser to look at alternative methods, and Fig. 1.4 shows one possible method.

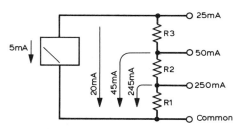

Fig. 1.4  Universal shunt.

The meter shown has a f.s.d. of ·5mA, an internal resistance of 40Ω, and is required to provide additional ranges of 25mA, 50mA, and 250mA. The circuit shown is commonly known as a universal shunt, and comprises resistors R1, R2, and R3. The *total* resistance of the shunt must be such that, on the *lowest* current range, 20mA passes through the resistors, leaving 5mA to pass through the meter, just as was done above.

The resistance of R1, R2, and R3, is given by

$$Rs = \frac{Im \text{ times } Rm}{Is} = \frac{0 \cdot 005 \text{ times } 40}{0 \cdot 02} = 10\Omega$$

The overall resistance, comprising the meter, R1, R2, and R3, is $40\Omega + 10\Omega = 50\Omega$. The next step is to calculate the value of the *highest* current shunt, R1. The meter requires only 5mA, so R1 must pass the excess of 245mA.

R1, R2, and R3 $= 10\Omega$, so we say that R2 + R3 = 10 − 1. The resistance of the meter side of the circuit, Rm, is = to 40 + (10 − R1) which can be rewritten as 50 − R1, resolving into an equation

$$R1 = \frac{0 \cdot 005(50 - R1)}{245} = 0 \cdot 245 \text{ R1} = 0 \cdot 250 - 0 \cdot 005R1$$

or R1 = to 1$\Omega$.

R2 is found similarly. R1 + R2 must now pass 45mA, still leaving 5mA for the meter. R1 (which we have just calculated to be 1$\Omega$) plus

$$R2 = \frac{0 \cdot 005 (49 - R2)}{0 \cdot 045} = 0 \cdot 045 + R2 = 0 \cdot 245 - 0 \cdot 005,$$

giving R2 as 4$\Omega$.

Having calculated R1 at 1$\Omega$ and R2 at 4$\Omega$, we can add them together to give 5$\Omega$, subtract this from the total resistance of 10$\Omega$, giving R3 as 5$\Omega$.

## Construction of Current Shunt Resistors

Having calculated the value of shunt resistors, for a given application, we are faced with procuring them. In the case of new, or reasonably new, meters the manufacturer can be approached, and will normally be able to supply shunts to suit, the accuracy being 1% or, at most, 2%. Shunts so obtained are frequently of the 'printed circuit' type, with current ranges of around 30 amps maximum. Such shunts, though very convenient as far as procurement is concerned, are still subject to the provisos mentioned earlier: inconvenience, loss, damage. Also, if multiple ranges are required, such shunts are not a really viable proposition, and will have to be abandoned in favour of a universal shunt. Yet again, it may be that for some reason or another ready-made shunts cannot be obtained. It is therefore useful to be able to make one's own shunts.

The construction of shunts is by no means difficult, but careful and painstaking workmanship is required if they are to have any pretensions to accuracy. The material used for shunts has to be carefully chosen; its resistance must be substantially unaffected by temperature, and it must possess negligible thermoelectric effects, i.e. it must not behave like a thermocouple if connected to, or by, a copper wire—normally used for interconnections. Manganin wire possesses both attributes, but is not easy to work. Eureka wire, or Constantan wire is reasonably easy to use, has a good coefficient of temperature, but is subject to appreciable thermo-electric effects.

However, provided that the junction with a copper wire is not subjected to heat (otherwise it will make a good, but totally undesired thermocouple!) and any soldering that is necessary is allowed ample time to cool down, Eureka or Constantan can be successfully used for shunts. It is also essential to use a substantial gauge of wire for heavy current shunts, to preclude the shunt heating up and acting as a thermocouple.

The resistance of the shunt has been calculated, and by reference to tables the gauge of Eureka or Constantan most suitable, or most easily available, is decided upon. Wires of most kinds, including resistance wires, are drawn to a surprising degree of accuracy, though 'normal' manufacturing tolerances have to have an effect. In the absence of an accurate resistance bridge, or accurate current meter covering the required range, a length can be cut, as accurately as possible, and then $\frac{1}{2}''$ is added at each end for soldering the shunt. This may suffice for rough and ready work, or where it cannot be avoided, but for really accurate work the length of the wire required must be determined as precisely as possible.

This can be by means of an accurate resistance bridge, in which case a somewhat longer length of wire than that calculated is connected across the terminals of the bridge. It is then gradually shortened until the exact length required is found. A bend is then made at each end to indicate the exact length, the surplus at each end can be reduced to $\frac{1}{2}''$, which should be sufficient for soldering the shunt onto its support.

In the absence of an accurate bridge, and remembering that most 'Ohmmeters' do not possess the requisite degree of accuracy, the circuit of Fig. 1.5 can be used. Again, the wire is cut somewhat longer than calculated, and is then connected in series with an ammeter having the requisite range and accuracy. An additional (series) variable resistor, may prove necessary. Finally, a battery can be connected.

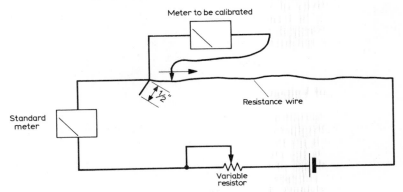

Fig. 1.5   Calibrating a shunt.

The meter to be shunted is not, at this stage, connected. The variable resistor is adjusted until the 'standard' meter reads full scale. Then the meter to be shunted, let us call it the 'unknown' meter, is now connected. One end of a flying lead is connected exactly ½″ from one end of the resistance, or shunt, wire, and the other flying lead is then connected near to it, and then is slid slowly towards the other end of the resistance wire, until such time as the unknown meter reads precisely the same as the standard meter.

At this point, a further ½″ is marked on the wire, which can then be cut. This end can be soldered to its support. When cool, the reading must be rechecked. It is absolutely essential to connect the battery, standard meter resistance wire, and variable resistor as shown, with the unknown meter tapped along the resistance wire. If contact is lost between the unknown meter and the resistance wire, no harm is done. But, if the resistance wire and unknown meter are interchanged, all the current can pass through the meter if contact with the wire is lost, and damage, or total destruction, of the meter will result.

## Measurement of Voltage

The moving coil meter is essentially a current-operated instrument. It can, however, be converted for use as a voltmeter by the use of suitably chosen series resistors, commonly known as multipliers. Again, we invoke Ohm's law, this time the $E = I$ times $R$ part. If we have a meter with a basic f.s.d. current of 1mA, and we connect a 10kΩ in series with it, we get $I \times 10k/0.001$ giving $E = 10$ volts.

If we now apply this to a supply of 10 volts, the meter will read full scale, assuming the supply is precisely 10 volts, the meter consumes precisely 1mA, and the resistor is precisely 10kΩ. If the voltage is, say, only 5 volts, the meter will read half scale. If the supply is greater than 10 volts, the meter will be driven off its scale, and if the supply is very much greater than 10 volts, the meter will probably suffer damage.

The sensitivity of voltmeters is commonly described, for no real good reason, in terms of the series resistance required for every volt to be measured, and our example would therefore be described as having a sensitivity of 10kΩ per volt, usually abbreviated to 10kΩ/V.

## Calculation of Voltage Multiplier Resistors

The above description can be clarified in the form of a short equation, which also introduces a factor not considered above: Rm = (E/I) − r, where Rm is the resistance of the multiplier, E is the voltage to be measured, I is the current consumption of the meter, and r is the internal resistance of the meter. This latter factor, r, is only significant at low voltages, where it is a significant proportion of the multiplier resistance. Let us look at an example.

Let E = 100 volts, I = 100μA, and r = 1kΩ. This gives us

$$Rm = \frac{100}{0\cdot0001} - 1k\Omega \text{ or } 999{,}000\Omega.$$

If we had neglected the effects of 'r', then Rm = 1MΩ and the difference as a percentage is low enough to be ignored. But if we substitute E = 1 volt, then the answer is completely different.

$$\frac{1}{0\cdot0001} - 1k\Omega, \text{ or } 9k\Omega.$$

If we neglect 'r', we get 10kΩ, and the difference is now appreciable. As a very good rule of thumb, if r is less than 1% of the overall multiplier resistance, it can be safely ignored. As the percentage increases, so do the errors introduced due to ignoring it.

Where more than one voltage range is required, more than one multiplier resistor will be required, and it becomes necessary to consider the various ways of connecting them into circuit. There are two basic ways, shown in Fig. 1.6a, b. They can be series connected, as in a, or individually connected as in b. The latter method is straightforward, and requires only that the individual resistors are calculated, obtained, and then connected either to the range switches

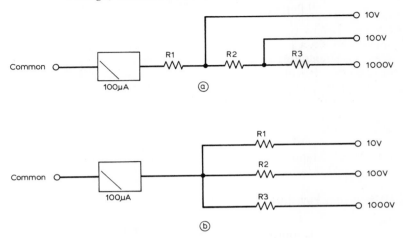

Fig. 1.6  Voltmeter connections.

or to sockets. The former, though a little more involved, is still quite simple. The resistors are calculated, as before, then the *lowest* resistor is connected into circuit. The next lowest comes next, but the value of the *previous* resistor must be subtracted from it. The next in line has the values of the two preceding resistors subtracted, and so on. A numerical example would help, so here it is.

Let us suppose that a 100μA meter is used, and must measure 10 volts, 100 volts, and 1000 volts. (Having just considered the effects of 'r' above, we can safely leave it out here, or it may confuse the issue instead of clarifying it!) We can calculate that resistors of 100kΩ, 1MΩ and 10MΩ are required, for R1, R2, and R3. R1 can be made the calculated value, but R2 must have R1 subtracted from it, giving 900kΩ. Similarly, R3 = 10MΩ − R1 + R2 = 9MΩ.

## Multiplier Resistors

The resistors used for voltage multipliers must have impeccable pedigrees if the meter is to be accurate and reliable. The resistors must have high initial accuracies—at least 1%—and must not alter to any appreciable degree with the passage of time or current. (Although we are measuring voltage it will be remembered that it is actually the passage of current that actuates the moving coil.) Wire wound resistors are frequently used for close tolerance −0·1% to 0·01%, and if they are properly made and aged, the stability is very good.

The best of the alternative resistors are the metal film types, which can be obtained to accuracies of 0·1%, with very stable temperature coefficients—typically 15 parts per million for every degree Centigrade of temperature rise, whilst long term stability is also very good at, typically, 50 parts per million over several years.

Carbon film resistors are also suitable for multipliers, but metal-oxide resistors are not so suitable. Whilst the initial accuracy is good, their temperature coefficients are inferior, and there is a tendency for thermoelectric effects to be set up between the body of the resistor and the end caps. The reliability of metal-film resistors is such that they are used in the highest grades of volt and test meters.

**Determining Meter Internal Resistance**

The calculations involving current shunt resistors and voltage multiplier resistors require that the internal resistance of the meter is known. This is sometimes printed on the meter, or can be obtained from the meter manufacturer. If the internal resistance cannot be discovered, it must be measured, and Fig. 1.7 shows how this can be done.

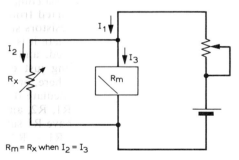

$R_m = R_x$ when $I_2 = I_3$

Fig. 1.7   Determining meter internal resistance.

The meter, in series with a variable resistor is connected across a battery, and the resistor is then adjusted to bring the meter pointer to *precisely* full scale. Next, a resistance (preferably an accurate decade resistance box, but a variable resistor will do) is connected across, i.e. in parallel with, the meter. The parallel resistor is now adjusted until the meter reads *precisely* half scale. The principle should now be emerging.

Half the current is passing through the meter, the other half through the resistor in parallel with the meter. Their resistances must therefore be equal. If the parallel resistor is a decade resistance box, the internal resistance can be determined to a high degree of accuracy. If it is a variable resistor, it should be measured on a bridge, failing that, on an Ohmmeter. Since meter coils are normally produced to a tolerance of $\pm 10\%$, it is a good idea to measure the resistance of the meter in any case.

An alternative method which gives the same result, but which may be easier to set up, is to connect a resistor as before across the meter, and to note the reading, which should ideally be mid-scale. The internal resistance is then:

$$Rm = \frac{X(i - I)}{I}$$

where Rm is the meter internal resistance, X is the known resistance in parallel with the meter, i is the f.s.d. rating of the meter, and I is the new reading.

### Measurement of Alternating Voltages

The moving coil meter, as we saw earlier, responds only to a direct current passing through the coil, and will not respond to an alternating current. However, by the addition of a suitable rectifier to turn the alternating current into a direct current, measurements can be made not only at the mains frequency of 50Hz, probably the most common task of the average alternating voltmeter, but also at the audio frequencies, and sometimes very much higher.

It is possible to use a single rectifier, as shown in Fig. 1.8. The output is a pulsating direct voltage, of either positive or negative polarity, depending on which way the rectifier is connected, varying

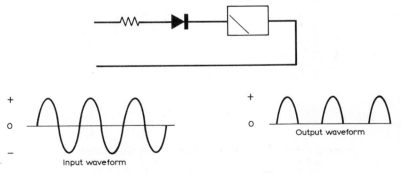

Fig. 1.8   The single wave rectifier.

from zero to the peak of the input voltage (assuming there are no losses in the rectifier). The inertia of the pointer and coil prevents the meter from reading the peak voltage, and it will therefore indicate mean values, which will be 0·318 of the peak values.

## The Bridge

An alternative, and more commonly used rectifier configuration, is the bridge, shown in Fig. 1.9. The arrows show the direction of current flow through the meter every time the polarity of the input voltage changes. Again, the output is a pulsating direct voltage, but at twice the mains—or other—frequency, due to there being two conduction cycles for every change in signal polarity. And, again, the inertia of the pointer and coil prevents the meter reading the peak value of the pulsating direct voltage.

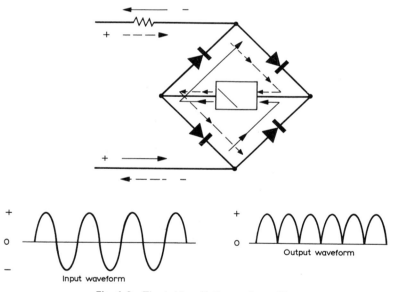

Fig. 1.9   The bridge (full-wave) rectifier.

The meter reads mean values and these will be 0·637 of the peak values. For the determination of series multiplier resistances, a more useful factor to know is the relationship to r.m.s. values, which are used for most meter scales. With a sinusoidal waveform, the reading is $2\sqrt{2}/\pi$ or 0·9 of the r.m.s. value. This relationship holds good only when the waveform is truly sinusoidal; any departure from a sinusoid will introduce errors in the reading.

When multiplier resistances are being calculated, a correction factor is necessary. The simplest way of doing this is to multiply the actual current consumption of the meter by 1·11, making a 100$\mu$A meter have an *apparent* consumption of 110$\mu$A.

## The Rectifier

The efficiency of copper-oxide rectifiers, once used exclusively, is one that decreases with increasing frequency, and such rectifiers were limited to frequencies of only a very few kHz. The use of semi-conductor devices of the silicon and germanium types has increased the upper limit greatly, and many modern multimeters will cover the audio frequencies with a good degree of accuracy.

Rectifiers, whilst conducting, drop a portion of the applied voltage across themselves, and this volts drop is dependent on the applied voltage resulting in the familiar curved characteristic seen on data sheets. This means that in practice a non-linear scale is obtained when the applied voltage is low. As the applied voltage is increased, the scale becomes more linear. The result can be seen in commercial multimeters, which are usually provided with two a.c. voltage scales, a non-linear one from, typically, 0–10 volts, and another linear scale from 10 volts upwards.

## Measurement of Alternating Current

For measuring a.c. current, most meters incorporate a transformer having a tapped primary by means of which the various a.c. ranges are obtained. The ratio of the secondary is usually designed to provide a voltage increase, and feeds the rectifier diodes in the same way as for a.c. voltage.

## Measurement of Resistance

The moving coil meter can be converted quite easily to measure yet another quantity, resistance. The accuracy attainable is not as high as that attainable by other methods, but it is good enough for many routine measurements, as well as being generally more convenient and less time consuming. Such instruments are known collectively as ohmmeters.

An ohmmeter is an instrument comprising a low consumption moving coil meter, a limiting resistor, a battery, and the resistor under test; a simple type is shown in Fig. 1.10. The variable resistor is necessary to set the meter at f.s.d. with the input terminals short circuited together.

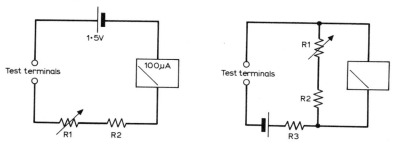

Fig. 1.10   (left)   Series ohmmeter with series set-zero variable resistor.

Fig. 1.11   (right)   Series ohmmeter with parallel set-zero variable resistor.

If the meter has a f.s.d. of $100\mu A$, the total value of the fixed and variable resistors must be such that f.s.d. is obtained, and if the battery is 1·5 volts, a common voltage, then the values must total at least 15kΩ, and in practice could be made up of 10kΩ for the variable, and 5–10kΩ for the fixed. If the unknown resistor is connected and gives, for example, a half scale reading, we can deduce that the *total* resistance must be 30kΩ, i.e. $1·5V/50\mu A$. Since we have 15kΩ in circuit already, the unknown must be 30k — 15k = 15kΩ.

Whenever the unknown resistor is connected into circuit, the current through the meter is reduced by an amount dependent on the unknown resistance. If the unknown, call it x, is equal to the sum of the meter resistance plus R1 + R2, the meter will read half scale as just shown. If x is less than the sum of Rm + R1 + R2, then the meter will read more than half scale; conversely if Rm + R1 + R2 is less than x the meter will read less than half scale.

The variable in Fig. 1.10 is necessary to compensate for the fall in battery voltage that accompanies much use and/or age. This circuit, for obvious reasons, is known as the series type.

**Alternative Ohmmeters**

An alternative type of ohmmeter circuit is shown in Fig. 1.11. Here, the zero is set by means of a variable resistor in parallel with the meter. In general, this circuit is more accurate than that of Fig. 1.10. In both these circuits, zero resistance is to the maximum current end of the scale, and maximum resistance is to the minimum current end of the scale, current zero indicating either a very high resistance, or open circuit terminals, or an open circuit resistor. Zero, in both types, is set with the terminals short circuited.

The third type of ohmmeter circuit is the shunt, or parallel, type, and is shown in Fig. 1.12. Here, the battery and adjusting resistor are in series with the meter, and the unknown resistor is connected in shunt, or parallel, with the meter, hence its name.

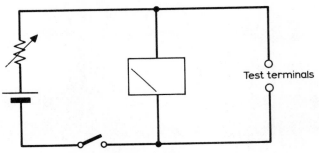

Fig. 1.12    Parallel (shunt) ohmmeter.

Zero is set with the terminals open-circuit and with the switch closed. The unknown resistor is connected, and if this is equal to the internal resistance of the meter, half the battery current will pass through the meter and half through the resistance, and the meter will read half scale.

If the unknown is less than the resistance of the meter, it will draw more current, the meter reading will drop, and so the lower resistances will be found towards the low current end of the scale, and the high resistances will be found at the high current end of the scale. The meter will read in opposition to the two previous circuits. The chief use of the shunt ohmmeter is in the measurement of low, and very low, resistances.

The value of the unknown resistance can be calculated with ease if we know a few facts. With the meter terminals short circuited, we obtain a current $I = E/R$. With the unknown connected, we obtain another reading, call it i, equal to $E/Rm + x$. By rearranging to get rid of 'E' we get the unknown x equal to $Rm (I/i - 1)$. In practice, it is not often that we have to calculate resistance values in this way, as ohmmeters come with ready-calibrated scales; nevertheless, it is useful to be able to do so if the occasion demands!

**Complete Test Meters**

The various circuits that moving coil meters can be used in have been looked at in some detail in the preceding pages. Such instruments can be very useful in their own right, and are frequently used in this way, usually mounted in desk stand cases. Three such instruments, by *BPL*, are shown in Fig. 1.13. These are, left to right, a centre zero 0–3, 0–10, and 0–30 volt meter, a 1mA meter, and a 1mA meter with a 1A printed circuit shunt. I use these in my home laboratory, and extremely useful they are.

Fig. 1.13    BPL desk stand meters.

However, it is more usual to find the voltage, current, and resistance measuring facilities all incorporated in a single instrument, when it is commonly referred to as a 'universal testmeter' or a 'universal multimeter', or, more commonly, simply abbreviated to 'multimeter'. In publications originating in the USA, the complete instrument is commonly referred to as a 'VOM', meaning 'Volt, Ohm, Milliameter'.

Nomenclature aside, the circuits of most multimeters follow well established design procedures, though here all similarity ends and there can be all the world of difference between the very best and the not-so-good, not the least, unfortunately, being the cost!

**Constructing a Multimeter**

It is perfectly feasible for the enthusiast to construct a first class multimeter, capable of a high degree of accuracy and reliability, provided he is capable and willing to indulge in some careful and painstaking work. The first requirement is a circuit, and a suitable one is shown in Fig. 1.14. This is not a complex circuit, nor does it offer a very wide range of services—many of which may never be used!—but it does provide an 'a.c. current' measuring facility, something even quite expensive multimeters do not, but one which is used quite often—once one knows it is there!

The current shunts are the only components deserving some men-

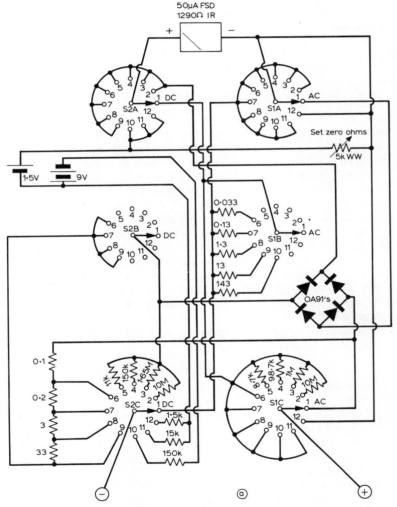

Fig. 1.14   (a)  Circuit of practical multirange meter.

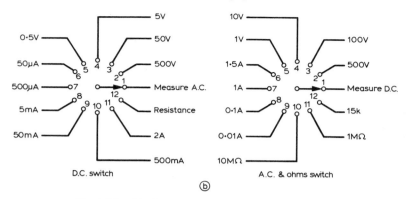

Fig. 1.14   (b)   Range switch details of Fig. 1.14 (a).

tion, since the design procedures outlined in earlier pages should suffice to outline the workings of the circuit. In the case of the shunt resistors, these *must* be constructed *in situ*, in order to allow for the small, but finite, contact resistances provided by the range switches. In a well designed and constructed switch, contact resistances should be reduced to only a very few milliohms, but even this apparently low figure assumes dangerous proportions when we consider that one of the shunt resistors is only 0·033Ω.

The circuit of Fig. 1.14 can be constructed using a different meter, and calculating the values of the series and shunt resistors can prove to be a most informative and rewarding exercise, if for no other reason than discovering how much of the previous information has been properly understood! Actually, constructing a multimeter has certain advantages; it can be 'tailor made' and so incorporate ranges and facilities not available commercially; it can be valuable instruction for apprentices, trainees, and others embarking in a career in electronics.

## Commercial Multimeters

Commercial multimeters can be obtained from a pound or two, to many tens of pounds. All other factors being equal, the old adage 'you only get what you pay for' is very true, and you must be prepared to pay handsomely for—even if it hurts—reliability and accuracy to the highest degree.

In between the very cheap and the very expensive multimeters, it is possible to find a range of instruments that will suffice for many routine measurements without landing one in the bankruptcy courts. Typical of these are the meters distributed by *Eagle*, which, unlike some of the importations from the far East, are excellent value for money, and if properly treated should give many years of reliable service.

Typical of the very highest grade of multimeters are the *Avo* model 8, which is now in its fifth mark, and the GEC *Selectest Super* 50, both of which I have come to regard with special affection over many years.

Multimeters having sensitivities of 100kΩ/V are, in general, somewhat of a rare breed, of which undoubtedly the best known is the *Taylor* model 100A. A less expensive multimeter, also at 100kΩ/V, is the *Eagle* model EP100LN.

## Choosing a Multimeter

By now the industrious reader should be in a position where he— or she!—can design multirange volt and current meters, and also

Fig. 1.15 The GEC *Selectest Super 50* multirange meter.

knows something of the fundamentals of other types of meters. Such knowledge *may* be purely academic, but it should have very important *practical* implications. But what of actually choosing a multimeter?

An injudiciously made purchase will be a source of continual future regret, for no supplier will exchange one multimeter for another. If money is no object, the safest course of action is to purchase a multimeter from a 'household name' manufacturer such as *Avo* or *GEC*. Since few amateurs are in this happy position, purchase must be preceded by a very thorough analysis of one's requirements, and it is interesting to consider the essentials.

The first factor to be considered is the application. For what may be very loosely termed 'power' engineering, sensitivities of $166\Omega/V$ are the norm, exemplified by the *Avo* model 40. 'General purpose' instruments are around $500–1000\Omega/V$, exemplified by the *Avo* model 7 and the GEC *Selectest Super K*. For electronics work, the multimeter must be very much more sensitive in order not to load the circuit under test, as explained in Chapter 2. The very minimum, is $10k\Omega/V$, but $20k\Omega/V$ has been the norm for many years, and most of the voltages quoted in manufacturer's circuits and data sheets specify that a $20k\Omega/V$ meter has been used. This, then, enables any one using the information to interpret the readings actually obtained in terms of the instrument being used.

Readers who have some of the older service sheets will see that very often two sets of figures were given, one for $1k\Omega/V$ and one for $20k\Omega/V$ instruments. On high impedance circuits, quite wide divergences can be seen, illustrating perhaps more graphically the effects of loading than mere abstract calculations can convey.

**Accuracy**

Since a multimeter is a *measuring* instrument, the primary requirement is that it must be accurate. A good multimeter will be accurate to $1\%$ or, at most, to $2\%$; cheaper meters will perforce have lower standards of accuracy at around $2\frac{1}{2}\%$ to $4\%$. Anything less is not worth considering; remember, we are considering *measuring* instruments. This accuracy is the *full scale* accuracy, or the amount the reading may deviate from the absolute value. As an example, suppose we are measuring a precise 100 volts. A $1\%$ meter will read between 99 volts and 101 volts, whilst the $4\%$ meter will read between 96 volts and 105 volts. The importance of a good degree of accuracy is therefore very apparent.

This deviation remains fixed in absolute value down the scale.

What this means in practical terms is that a reading made at one tenth of full scale will deviate from the absolute value by ± ten times the full scale accuracy, i.e. a 1% meter has now deteriorated to ±10%. For this reason, all good multimeters have overlapping scales so that the pointer can be kept at the top end of the scale where accuracy is highest.

It is little good having a very accurate multimeter unless it can be absolutely relied upon to maintain its accuracy indefinitely, even if subjected to improper treatment. The term 'built like a battleship' is often used in a derogatory manner, but any multimeter that fits this description should be looked upon with favour. It may not be 'pretty', but it should be useful long after the pretty multimeters have been subjected to the scrap heap!

### Meter Scales

Meter scales are frequently scaled in the sequence of 1–2–5 or 1–3–10; both allow the pointer to be kept well up the scale, and both allow

Fig. 1.16   The latest Avo Model 8 test meter.

easy mental increase or decrease by the appropriate factor when changing ranges, a feat that is rendered more difficult by some manufacturers who choose ranges the ratios of which are not whole numbers. (This does not apply to dB scales which are in the ratio of 1:316 in meters having a 1–3–10 sequence.)

Some manufacturers also cram a multitude of scales onto the dial, making it difficult to take readings without suffering eyestrain, and which inevitably increase the chances of making incorrect readings. Such scales may impress the novice, or may delight the individual who exults in mental gymnastics, but practicing engineers prefer the type of clear straight forward scale as used by *Avo* and *GEC* in their respective instruments.

The facilities an instrument can offer, as advertised, are frequently most impressive. However extensive these may be, however, it is a certain fact that any one instrument can only be in one place at a time and perform one task at a time. After very careful consideration, it may become apparent that it may be advantageous to purchase two cheaper meters than one expensive one. If it is certain that one multimeter will suffice, then it is very clearly desirable to purchase the very best that can be afforded, as such an instrument will prove to be a long term investment, and the cost, if equated—as it really ought to be—in terms of years of service, will turn out to be negligible.

**Obtaining a Multimeter**

A multimeter can be obtained from a reputable supplier as the product of a reputable manufacturer; it can be home made; it can be purchased as a kit of parts for self assembly; it can be purchased second-hand. We have just looked at commercial multimeters, and sufficient was said to enable the reader to form his own opinions, and a little earlier we looked at the circuit of a multimeter suitable for home, or laboratory, construction. That leaves us with purchasing a kit of parts, or purchasing a second-hand multimeter.

In the UK, the principal supplier of kits of all types is *Heath Schlumberger*, an American company based at Gloucester. They supply the MM-IU multimeter kit. This is a 20kΩ/V (d.c.) and 5kΩ/V (a.c.) instrument, covering from 1·5V f.s.d. to 1·5kV f.s.d. This is a good example of its type, with the advantage that its construction is as fool-proof as anything of this nature can be.

There are dangers in purchasing anything second-hand, and in the case of multimeters the very best advice is 'don't', unless you *know* either the instrument or the seller. If it appears to be a bargain (and few of us can really resist those!) try to check it very carefully against a multimeter known to be accurate. Check that the pointer doesn't stick—and if you've never stripped a meter leave well alone, or your repair bill may be that much greater—and your 'bargain' will have cost you a small fortune—and that none of the ranges is open circuit, intermittent, or wildly out of tolerance. Then try to arrange a 'money back' type of guarantee. And all this *before* parting with your money!

## Care of Multimeters

A multimeter is a delicate and precision instrument, and must be treated as such. The biggest enemies of multimeters—of any meters— are vibration, shock, extremes of temperature, dust and grit, humidity and damp, and all of these can be successfully guarded against by the application of common sense. When carrying or handling such instruments, treat them as if they were mugs of beer full to the brim and in danger of spilling!

In use, try to ensure that the instrument is never overloaded, and if it is, inevitably, then try to have it checked immediately; the 'signs' of damage are not always visible. All good quality multi-meters have some form of overload protection; either an electro-mechanical cut-out, which if properly designed is virtually infallible; diodes across the meter movement, offering some protection to the meter movement but not to associated components, and subject to being burnt out; and fuses which offer, again, limited protection, but which, once they have ruptured render the circuit open-circuit. It is nice to know that protection is there, but like life insurance try to avoid cashing in! In all cases, follow the manufacturers instructions implicitly—he hasn't put them there for decoration.

## Use of Multimeters

Since all moving coil meters depend on current to operate their coils, it follows that they will extract a current, however minute, from the circuit under test, and will 'load' that circuit, causing some errors to be introduced in the readings made. If this is always borne in mind, due allowances can be made, and cross checks carried out. A very useful rule of thumb is to neglect the effects of meter current if the current flowing in the circuit is at least 100 times greater, i.e. a current of 5mA for a $50\mu A$ f.s.d. meter.

If the circuit current is less, a cross check should be instituted, such as measuring the current in the collector circuit (or anywhere else, depending on the circuit) from which the volts drop can be calculated, and the cross check is there. Then record the reading for future reference. The effects of meter loading are discussed in some detail in Chapter 2.

It is not uncommon to see multimeters propped up at all angles with readings being taken, and then relied upon as absolute Gospel. This is bad practice, for whilst many multimeters will provide *reasonable* accuracy at indeterminate angles, they are almost always constructed to provide *maximum* accuracy at some *specified* angle, frequently horizontally. If the manufacturer has taken the trouble to specify the angle providing maximum accuracy, it is only wise to adhere to his recommendations, unless circumstances dictate otherwise, of course.

**Reading Scales**

The subject of reading multimeters leads us nicely on to the subject of reading meter scales. These should be, as explained earlier, clear open scales, free from ambiguity. It is essential to interpret them correctly, and not attribute to them a degree of accuracy the manufacturer probably never intended. If this sounds like a contradiction in terms, consider the recording of a reading to two decimal places, as for example 17·40, instead of the correct 17·4.

The two readings are *numerically absolutely identical*, so what's the difference? It is, quite simply, one of implied—albeit innocent—accuracy. 17·4 means that the actual quantity may vary from 17·35 to 17·45, a variation of $\pm 0.05$. But 17·40 means that the actual quantity may vary from 17·395 to 17·405, a variation of $\pm 0.005$, or an order of accuracy *ten times better than the former example*, even though the numerical values, as just explained, are absolutely identical. This is an example of *false accuracy*, but a very easy pitfall to drop into.

**Permissible Error**

All measuring instruments are provided with a pedigree, however sketchy or doubtful, stating the limits of permissible error. A most important factor is never specified for accuracy, yet it is the most variable and capricious factor. This is the human element, the instrument operator! He may be 100% reliable, or his unreliability may run into many places of decimals! Yet we all make mistakes, and so it behoves us all to take extra care, but *not* to the point of obsession!

Handling instruments and taking readings is a combination of knowledge and common sense, allied to a methodical and consistent procedure. Consistency ensures that experiments can be repeated with every chance of success, that former readings will be repeated; in short, errors and mistakes can be discovered by working backwards, or by recovering old ground. Lack of consistency will certainly ensure that errors will remain safely hidden; other errors will occur; one error will mask another.

**Measuring A.C.**

When using the a.c. ranges of a multimeter, remember that it may, if a little elderly, use copper-oxide rectifiers, and the characteristics of these do change with age or mis-use. Also, the frequency response will be severely curtailed. Modern multimeters using silicon or germanium rectifiers will remain stable indefinitely, unless severely overloaded; also their frequency response is very much better. Most manufacturers state the frequency response of their instruments. This deteriorates on the high voltage ranges due to stray capacities, and severely on the current ranges due to losses in the transformer—where one is used.

On the a.c. volts ranges, there is usually still d.c. continuity, which means that the meter will read, albeit incorrectly, if connected across a source of d.c. voltage. The polarity of the applied voltage will not matter, since the bridge rectifier normally used will 'route' the current correctly. This means that the multimeter must be connected with care into any circuit containing d.c. volts, for this will vitiate any readings made. If there is *any* doubt, or if d.c. voltage *is* present, at the point where a.c. volts must be measured, then it is essential to connect a capacitor in series with the multimeter.

The capacitance of this capacitor must be high enough to preclude any errors due to its inclusion, remembering that the reactance of a capacitor is inversely proportional to frequency. It must also have a suitably high working voltage, so that it does not breakdown. Electrolytic capacitors are unsuitable because of their inherently high leakage current, and the magnitude of this leakage, and unwanted, current may very easily exceed the magnitude of the a.c. it is desired to measure.

Finally, remember that the capacitor, whatever its value, will pass an appreciable surge current when first connected across d.c. volts, and so start on the highest voltage range of the multimeter and then slowly 'work' down, allowing the capacitor time to re-charge every time the range is changed. This is indeed a risky procedure, and it is essentially one to be adopted when no more suitable instrument is available.

## Test Circuit Considerations

When using a multimeter—or any meter—to measure *current* in a circuit, remember that it connects in *series* with the current carrying circuit. *Voltage* measurements are, of course, made with the *voltmeter* in *parallel* with the circuit. The leads used to connect the multimeter to the circuit under test also possess inductance, particularly if they are of the not infrequently seen round-the-houses variety. They also possess capacitance.

Both properties may not affect some circuits; on others they, or one of them, may have disastrous results, provoking, or preventing, oscillations, instability, and other esoteric effects. It *may* be possible to reduce, possibly even eliminate, such effects by using leads as short as possible. In practice it means that several sets of leads will be required. I use several sets myself, ranging from 12″ long to some 36″ long. These leads should be made up using the ultra flexible wire available for these applications.

Decoupling the leads may help—or may make matters worse! Sometimes a 'suck-it-and-see' approach must be used as no two sets of circumstances are precisely the same. This is where an orderly consistent procedure, recommended earlier, is most valuable. It is also helpful to record *all* circuit details and all meter readings in a note book, as memory can be a most perverse and fickle 'assistant'. These readings can then be referred to, comparisons made, frequently enabling the right conclusions to be drawn. Perhaps more important, information, learning, and experience will be gained.

Long meter leads can also introduce stray couplings into a circuit, either from another part or from adjacent mains wiring. They are also mechanically dangerous. I well remember an expensive multimeter—my own as well!—that I pulled off a bench and damaged. As I walked away from the bench, the leads mysteriously got entangled in my clothing and the meter tried to follow me.

CHAPTER TWO

# ELECTRONIC METERS

---

THE MOVING COIL METER, as we saw in Chapter 1, was supreme in its versatility, culminating in its use in meters, and multimeters, of all types. Such instruments will adequately fulfil many requirements, and will suffice for most of the routine measurements that have to be made. The moving coil meter is not, however, without its limitations, and it is essential to know just what these are, for when they are reached, more sophisticated (and hence more expensive) instruments will be required, and a little delving into these limitations will be very rewarding.

**Effect of Internal Resistance**

The ideal *current* meter would have zero internal resistance, so that it did not introduce any volts drop into the circuit into which it was connected. But, as we saw in Chapter 1, it requires a finite *voltage* across it for the field developing current to be developed. Typical f.s.d.'s range from some tens of mV to several hundreds of mV, and it is quite possible for a meter to read low simply because of this volts drop. The following hypothetical—but quite possible—example shows why.

Suppose we connect a resistor of 1250Ω across a voltage such that the resistor passes precisely 100µA, as *calculated* by Ohm's law. We now connect a 100µA meter in series, possibly expecting it to read the calculated 100µA. But it does not, and reads only 50µA. Why? A quick mental calculation tells us that 50µA drawn from the previous mythical voltage source means that there is a total of 2500Ω in circuit. Since we have already accounted for 1250Ω, the remaining 1250Ω can only be in the meter itself, and in fact this is the resistance of the coil of many 100µA meter movements. The effects of meter internal resistance may not always be as drastic

31

as that given, but they are always there and must be always allowed for.

## Effect of Test Circuit

Just as an ideal current meter should have zero internal resistance, so that there is no voltage lost across the coil, so should an ideal *voltmeter* have infinite internal resistance so that it will not extract any current from the circuit under test. But the coil requires current to actuate it, and in the voltmeter this must be provided by the circuit under test. The error so caused is wholly dependent on the current flowing in the circuit, and on the current drawn by the meter. It is best explained by an example, this time accompanied by diagrams, starting with Fig. 2.1.

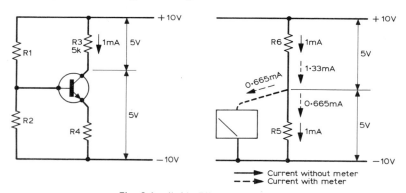

Fig. 2.1    (left)    Effect of test circuit.

Fig. 2.2    (right)    Effects of meter loading.

This shows a transistor biased in the conventional manner, passing a collector current of 1mA through the 5kΩ collector load resistor, which thereby drops 5 volts across itself leaving a collector-to-negative potential of 5V. The transistor can be conveniently regarded as a 'resistor' also having a value of 5kΩ including R4, and forming, in conjunction with R3, a potential divider as shown in Fig. 2.2. Here 5 volts is dropped across each resistor. On occasions we have to make certain assumptions, and this is one of them, so we *know* that the mid-point potential is exactly 5 volts.

We now try to measure the potential at this point using a some what elderly 1000Ω/volt meter set to its 5V f.s.d. range. We do *not* get the expected reading and wonder why? The 'equivalent resistance' of the transistor, we have seen, is 5kΩ, and, neglecting the internal resistance of the meter coil, the series resistance of the voltmeter is also 5kΩ, the two resistances being in parallel. We can calculate, mentally, by Ohm's Law, that the *effective* resistance is halved. The 5kΩ of R3 *plus* the 2500Ω of the meter plus transistor now gives us 7500Ω across the supply of 10V, so that the original current of 1mA is increased to 10/7500 = 1·33mA. R3 will now drop 1·33 × 5kΩ = 6·65 volts, leaving 3·35 volts across the transistor, or R5 of Fig. 2.2, and *not* the 5 volts we expected to find, an error of some considerable magnitude.

We can consider the same conditions again, but this time using a meter of 20kΩ/volt, the accepted norm in electronics engineering. The maths are unchanged, and are left to the reader. There is, again, an error, but much less than before. Similarly, we can calculate the effects of using a meter of 100kΩ/V, the most sensitive generally available. Again, there is an error, but it is less than with the 20kΩ/V meter, and considerably less than with the 1kΩ/V meter.

To carry the argument to its only conclusion, so long as a volt meter extracts power, however minute, from a circuit, errors will be caused, but after a certain point—which changes with the individual's outlook!—the error is only of pure academic interest, and the common sense criteria outlined in Chapter 1 can be safely applied.

## Other Limitations

Apart from the limitations we have just looked at, moving coil meters possess other limitations which restrict their usefulness. For d.c. applications, the lowest voltage that can be measured, in terms of f.s.d., is the f.s.d. voltage for that meter movement, and that will be unlikely to be less than some tens of mV, and our old friend the loading effect will rear its ugly head more likely than not! On a.c. matters are even worse. Multimeters with f.s.d's below some 2 or 2·5V are uncommon; most hover around the 10V mark. Also, there is d.c. continuity on the a.c. ranges, which means that it is not possible to measure, directly, an a.c. superimposed on a d.c., i.e. the ripple voltage of a d.c. power supply.

## Frequency Response

The *reliable* frequency response of most multimeters does not exceed a few kHz, or at most to a few tens of kHz, limiting their usefulness on high frequency circuits.

All these limitations (strictly speaking, these are not really limitations, for the multimeters are then being used outside their original terms of reference) call for other types of measuring instruments when work has to be done on circuits that will not tolerate any form of 'loading', or where very low voltages, or high frequencies (in this context, high frequencies refer to the audio and low radio frequencies) are involved. These 'other' measuring instruments form a most invaluable and important part of the armoury of the electronic engineer, or enthusiast, whose interest lead him into realms where the ordinary multimeter is not suitable.

## D.C. Electronic Meters

For the measurement of voltages on high impedance circuits, i.e. high resistance, low current circuits, or for the measurement of low, or very low voltages, some form of amplifier is clearly needed, and since this enables a basically low resistance meter to be connected into a high impedance circuit, such an amplifier is commonly known as an impedance transformer, or impedance convertor.

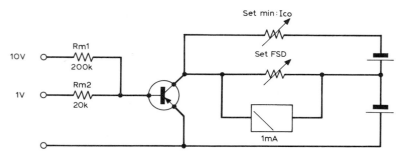

Fig. 2.3   Simple transistor voltmeter.

A very simple, but workable, meter amplifier is shown in Fig. 2.3. This utilises the current amplification properties of a transistor, and provides current gains of (typically) 20 times. The 1mA meter in Fig. 2.3 is thereby converted from a basic sensitivity of $1000\Omega/V$ to $20,000\Omega/V$. In its favour are simplicity and low cost; against it, a degree of inherent lack of stability due to changing transistor characteristics, particularly if the transistor is a germanium one.

Since a meter amplifier that is prone to drift is of doubtful value, it is necessary to investigate other forms of meter amplifier. The simplest of these is the bridge, or balanced, amplifier, shown in Fig. 2.4. Here, we have two transistors with the meter connected between their collectors. In conjunction with the two collector load

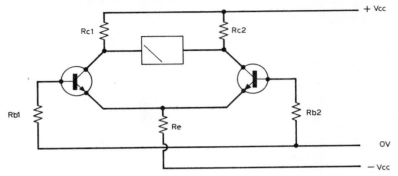

Fig. 2.4   Bridge, or balanced, amplifier.

resistors (Rc1, Rc2) they form a bridge, which, assuming that the components either side are exactly the same, will remain balanced, no current will flow, and the meter will read zero. A voltage applied across either base resistor (Rb) will cause a current to flow through the appropriate transistor, the bridge will be unbalanced, and the meter will indicate the current flowing, and, of course, can be calibrated in terms of the applied voltage. If the components are exactly the same either side, drift due to changing characteristics will tend to be the same, to cancel out, and the overall effect is one of improved stability, and the circuit is of some limited use.

**Amplifier Balance**

In practice, however, it is impossible to ensure equality of components, and so some means have to be provided to counteract the effects of component inequality, resulting in initial unbalance, and subsequent imbalance due to drifting characteristics. Passive components (i.e. resistors) can be obtained to very close tolerances, and with very stable thermal characteristics at the currents and voltages involved. This leaves the transistors as the main source of worry.

The transistor characteristics that are of particular interest here are $V_{be}$, $_{hfe}$, and $I_{cbo}$. Transistors can be obtained matched to within a few percent for $V_{be}$ and $_{hfe}$, and since the effects of $I_{cbo}$ will normally tend to cancel out, it is sufficient to provide means of finally equalising $V_{be}$ and $_{hfe}$. This is simply effected, as the circuit of Fig. 2.5 shows.

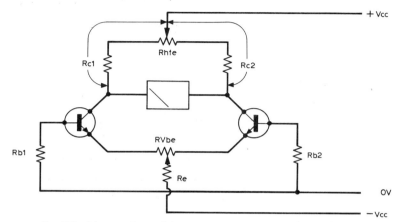

Fig. 2.5   Means of equalising Vbe and hfe of balanced amplifier.

This is similar to that of Fig. 2.4, with the addition of two variable resistors, $R_{hfe}$, and $RV_{be}$. The former equalises for $_{hfe}$ differences, the latter for Vbe differences. RVbe is initially adjusted for zero reading with the two bases temporarily shorted together. The short is removed, and zero is restored by means of $R_{hfe}$. The purpose of Re in the emitter circuit is to provide a degree of negative feedback; any increase in the emitter current of either transistor will increase the voltage across Re, so pushing the other transistor's emitter voltage up.

### Single-ended Circuit

Both the circuits considered so far are of the differential type, in which an input can be applied to either transistor and will cause the meter to read, the only difference being that the direction of current flow will be different. For some applications, a differential voltmeter is not only useful, but essential. For most of our applications, how-ever, it is essential that the circuit is single ended, i.e. an input is applied to one transistor base only, and that any signal common to both inputs is rejected.

The degree of rejection is measured in decibels, as a ratio, and is dependent on the values of Rc and Re, the relationship being approximately Rc/(2Re). This means that in order to obtain a high degree of rejection a high value of Re is required. A signal applied to both inputs simultaneously is known as a common mode signal, and the degree of rejection is known as the common mode rejection ratio, often abbreviated to cmrr.

In practice, it is not possible to have a high value for Re, since the voltage dropped across it is 'lost' as far as the rest of the circuit is concerned, unless a very high supply voltage is used. This is usually impracticable, and so it is necessary to seek an alternative means of providing a high value for Re. This is not too difficult, fortunately, and is illustrated in Fig. 2.6.

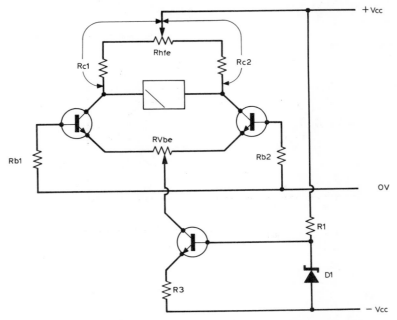

Fig. 2.6  Transistor used as a constant current source.

This is essentially similar to Fig. 2.5, but the emitter resistor Re has been replaced by a transistor, connected as a constant current source, the base voltage of which is held constant by the zener diode DI. The collector output resistance of the constant current source is very high, up to several megohms being common, when 'viewed' by the emitters of the balanced pair. Since this is very much higher than any usable resistor, the cmrr is correspondingly increased.

## High-gain Amplifiers

The circuits so far considered are fairly primitive, but like many primitive circuits are capable of being developed into comprehensive and even complex, circuits. A logical development is to add further transistors to obtain more gain, and a representative circuit is shown in Fig. 2.7. This is effectively similar to the previous circuits, but the addition of two further transistors increases the gain so that it is possible to obtain sensitivites of 20MΩ/V, i.e. a current gain of 1000 times when a 50μA meter is used.

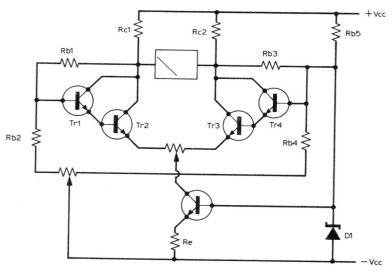

Fig. 2.7   High-gain amplifier.

Such very high current or voltage gains cannot be obtained without paying some penalties. The biggest problem is drift due to a change in a physical quantity, such as the gain of a transistor, or in a resistance. The main cause of drift is due to a change in temperature, particularly if applied to balanced amplifiers at different rates. The circuit of Fig. 2.7 serves admirably to illustrate this effect. If either Tr1 or Tr4—but not both—is warmed, or cooled, then the zero, or whatever the reading happened to be, will be seen to drift, and the rate and amount of drift will be dependent not only on the temperature imbalance, but also on the length of time the temperature imbalance is allowed to persist.

Restoring temperature equality, by either warming, or cooling, the transistor originally affected will restore the original reading. Such thermal effects can be minimised by selecting only special low current silicon transistors for these applications, and by placing 'opposite' pairs of transistors in very close physical proximity. A better scheme is to use special clips, which enable pairs of transistors to be clipped together. Still better, when absolutely certain that nothing requires changing, is to 'pot' the transistors in one of the special silicone rubber compounds. The ultimate development of this is the integrated circuit.

## Multi-transistor Circuits

While Fig. 2.7 is shown with n-p-n transistors, it is possible, though not common, to use p-n-p transistors. An extension of this circuit is the 'ring-of-three' where three transistors are used either side of the meter, either with similar polarities all round or a mixture of polarities for level shifting. Cascaded circuits are also used where pairs of transistors, as in Fig. 2.4, feed further pairs of transistors.

Again, n-p-n or p-n-p transistors, or a combination, can be used, and can provide very high current, and voltage, gains. Level shifting, by means of transistors of different polarities, is necessary to get round the problem of a build up of voltage levels when transistors of a similar polarity are used in multi stage amplifiers. This effect of voltage build up is a cumulative effect, and gets worse the more transistors are concerned, as the following, simplified, explanation shows.

Imagine three n-p-n or p-n-p transistors in a direct coupled configuration, where the collector of the first transistor feeds the base of the second, and the collector of the second feeds the base of the third transistor. For correct operation, the first transistor has its collector a given voltage above the earth level. This is the base voltage of the second transistor, and it too has its collector set a certain level above earth, but this level has to be above that of the collector of the first transistor. The same situation exists between the second and third transistors.

Now, for maximum undistorted output, the collector of a transistor has to be able to swing from virtually supply voltage to virtually its emitter voltage. But, because of the cumulative $V_{ce}$ (voltage, collector to emitter) effect, we can easily end up in a situation where the collector voltage of the third transistor is virtually at supply voltage, and its emitter voltage—assuming the usual emitter resistor —is well up, too. The maximum undistorted output is then greatly curtailed, and may possibly defeat the whole point of the circuit.

If a transistor with an opposite polarity is inserted between the first and third transistors, the 'middle' voltage is in 'opposition' to the other two, and the collector-to-earth voltages of the first and third transistors can be made, if desired, equal. We still have the full amplification possible, but because of the level shifting made possible by the 'odd' middle transistor, we also can obtain the maximum undistorted output possible.

Compound transistor amplifiers can provide current, or voltage gains, of several thousands of times, or tens of thousands of times, and are frequently used for this purpose. When used to increase the sensitivity of a voltmeter, as in Fig. 2.7 they can be most useful, provided care is taken to reduce drift to a minimum, or provided one is prepared to tolerate a certain amount of drift. For fairly low voltage gains, but at very high input resistance, the FET or field effect transistor is becoming increasingly popular, either used on its own or preceding bipolar transistors.

**FET Amplifiers**

A very simple meter amplifier using an FET is shown in Fig. 2.8. Although simple, this is quite a useful circuit, and is capable of providing an acceptable performance provided one does not expect it to replace much more sophisticated, and therefore more expensive, circuits. The FET forms, in conjunction with R5, R6, VR1 and R7, a bridge circuit. The current flowing in the source of the FET

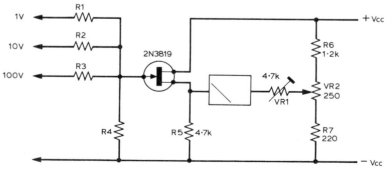

Fig. 2.8   Meter circuit using a FET.

sets up a voltage across R5, and VR1 is adjusted so that the voltage at its wiper is equal to the source voltage, at which point the meter reads zero.

If a voltage is now applied to the gate of the FET, the source current increases, increasing the voltage across R5, and the meter will register the difference in the voltage at the source of the FET and at the wiper of VR1. Provided the FET source resistor R5 is selected having regard to the characteristics of the FET, good linearity can be obtained, with an f.s.d. value of around 200 to 300mV. VR2 is set for a given f.s.d. value on the most sensitive range.

Other circuits using FETs follow quite closely on the configurations shown in Figs. 2.4, 2.5, 2.6. It is also common practice to use FETs to precede bipolar transistors, although integrated circuits are now tending to replace discrete transistors. Integrated circuits are also available, providing in one convenient package, FETs complete with following bipolar transistors.

### FET/IC Amplifier

A very useful circuit using a combination of FETs and an integrated circuit is shown in Fig. 2.9. The FETs must be matched as closely as possible for Idss, and should be mounted in a common clip for minimum thermal drift. The integrated circuit is the well known '741' available from a number of manufacturers. The voltage gain is dependent on the ratio of R1 to R2, and can be made as high as

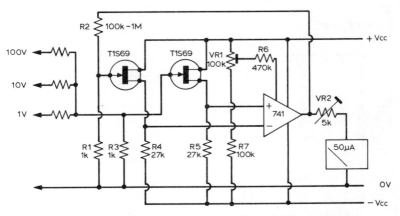

Fig. 2.9   Meter circuit using a combination of FETs and an IC.

60dB or 1000 times, although a more useful figure would be around 200 times, allowing f.s.d. values of as low as one millivolt, when used with a 50μA meter.

Even if the FETs are closely matched, some imbalance is inevitable. The IC also has a certain offset voltage that has to be allowed for, and both these effects can be cancelled out by means of VR1, so that the output is truly zero when there is no input. In practice, the gain is made a little greater than is theoretically required, and final 'trimming' to give a required meter reading for any given input is effected by VR2. If R3 is made, for example, 1000Ω, and the most sensitive range required is 1mV, then the multiplier resistors can be very simply calculated on the basis of 1MΩ/V.

This is an extremely useful and adaptable circuit, and one that can form the basis of a very comprehensive transistorised direct voltage multimeter. By the addition of suitable shunt resistors, a very wide ranged direct current multimeter can be constructed, since the basic f.s.d. current sensitivity is only 1μA. Suitable switching can be incorporated, to enable currents from 1μA upwards, and 1mV upwards, to be measured, but this is an exercise I will leave the reader to perform for himself!

### Chopper Amplifier

The last type of direct voltage meter to be considered is somewhat specialised. This is the 'chopper' type amplifier capable of measuring microvolts and nanoamps ($10^{-9}$A). The elements of this are shown in Fig. 2.10. The current to be measured is applied across the resistor R1. R2 and switch S are in series, and the output is taken from their junction, via C to the amplifier. Switch S is opened and closed very

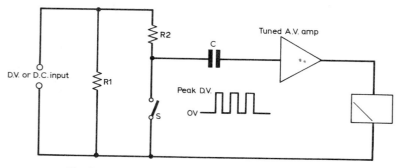

Fig. 2.10   Basic elements of chopper type amplifier.

rapidly, typically 200 to 400Hz, and the output therefore consists of a squarewave alternating between zero and the peak of the applied direct voltage.

The amplifier can be a relatively simple tuned amplifier, the centre frequency of which must, of course, correspond to the switching frequency of S. While the principle is quite straightforward, complications—of course—are frequently encountered. Thermo-electric effects and stray pickups from the switch energising oscillator can cause the meter to read in the absence of a signal, or can cause errors in the reading actually obtained.

Very careful screening can reduce pickup effects, and precious metal contacts can reduce thermo-electric effects. Drift, due to contact wear causing changes in the mark/space ratio can be troublesome. Sealed reed switches are frequently used as they can be obtained with suitable contacts, and, since a coil can be easily obtained to surround the switch, can be operated from alternating currents from a suitable oscillator.

Instruments have been made to operate from the *basic circuit* of Fig. 2.10, but it is also possible to substitute the mechanical switch with an electronic one consisting of a semiconductor device— transistor or FET—in parallel with the input signal with its base— or gate—fed with a squarewave from a squarewave generator so that the collector—or drain—current is alternatively cut-off and saturated. An instrument that does this very successfully is the Avo electronic Avometer type EA113. The FET in this instrument is an MPF103, and the squarewave generator is a pair of BC183 transistors operating in the astable mode.

## Alternating Voltage Electronic Meters

Earlier in this chapter, we saw the need for more sophisticated measuring instruments, the proof being in the way of direct voltage measurements, backed up by Fig. 2.1 and Fig. 2.2. A very similar situation exists when a.c. voltages must be measured in similar conditions, and the figures quoted could very well apply to a.c. voltages. In this case, however, the situation is complicated by the requirements of adequate frequency response when the audio, radio, and very high frequencies are concerned. We also saw that low, and very low, direct voltages are not easily measured, and the same can very well apply to alternating voltages, with a few added complications thrown in for good measure.

Electronic a.c. voltmeters work on two basic principles: rectifier/ amplifier, and amplifier/rectifier. The first, as the name suggests, is a rectifier followed by an amplifier, though the degree of amplification required can be very low. This is due to the characteristics of the diode which requires that several hundreds of mV are impressed across it before it begins to conduct, and several hundred more before it enters the most linear part of its characteristic.

The amplifier can be more properly regarded as an impedance transformer in this application, the maximum sensitivity being limited by the diode. This rules out the rectifier/amplifier instrument for low level work, except for some very sophisticated—and therefore expensive—instruments, but for 'radio' frequencies into the GHz region it does rule supreme.

For these applications, the diode is commonly of the thermionic type, as it is more abuse-resistant than its semiconductor counterparts, and is always mounted right in the tip of the probe so that it can be put to work with the minimum of circuit disturbance, since the stray and input capacitances are reduced to a very few pF. It is essential to ensure that the electron transit time within the diode is several orders of magnitude lower than the highest frequency to be measured, otherwise errors will occur.

### Amplifier/Rectifier Meter

The second type of meter is the amplifier/rectifier, and is very suitable for very low to very high a.c. voltage measurement, albeit at a greatly reduced frequency range, more specifically the audio and low radio frequencies. There are two basic problems to be solved in this application: the design of an amplifier that will handle without favour, or disfavour, the whole of the band of frequencies it is desired to measure, i.e. a truly aperiodic amplifier; and a rectifier that is free from non-linearity.

Negative feedback, the panacea for many electronic ailments and shortcomings, is pressed in to service to provide a linear scale, in spite of the attempts of the rectifier diodes. The effect of the negative feedback is to provide a virtually perfect current waveform, irrespective of the non-linear properties of the diodes. Fig. 2.11 shows the essentials. A full-wave rectifier is essential, and is connected between the output of the amplifier and resistor $R_F$. The voltage developed across $R_F$ is fed back to the amplifier in anti-phase, thereby alleviating the errors due to diode non-linearity.

For maximum linearity in the amplifier, it is desirable to limit the voltage excursions in it, and matters are normally arranged such that suitable attenuators are incorporated in front of the amplifier, so that the voltage presented to it is virtually constant, in spite of the

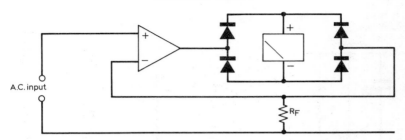

Fig. 2.11    Basic arrangement of amplifier/rectifier meter.

varying voltages that may be actually present at the input to the attenuators.

**Primary and Secondary Attenuators**

For maximum circuit convenience, it is not uncommon to find that the attenuator is split into two parts, a coarse or primary attenuator at the front line with a ratio of 1000:1 (giving 'volts' and 'millivolts') followed by some form of impedance convertor, then a secondary attenuator providing the actual voltage divisions, and lastly the main amplifier, as shown in Fig. 2.12. This is the basis of many designs, both commercial and amateur, and as such deserves a little further study.

If, as is common practice, the maximum sensitivity is 1mV, then this is the gain the main amplifier will have to provide, to make up the difference to the f.s.d. requirements of the meter movement. The impedance convertor does not normally provide any gain, its 'gain' being either unity or a little below unity. Inputs exceeding 1mV will have to be suitably attenuated, and this is the purpose of the secondary attenuator, which is shown as having steps of 1–3–10 up to 300mV. Other steps can also be used, 1–2–5 being also popular. If the voltmeter is to be used for plotting response curves, a common task, then the 1–3–10 sequence is usually modified a little to give a ratio between steps of 10dB or $1:\sqrt{10}$, i.e. $1:316$.

Levels above the range of the secondary attenuator, in this instance 300mV, are attenuated by the primary attenuator by a factor of 1000 times. For inputs of 1000mV (1 volt) or less, therefore, the primary attenuator is left in its 'divide by one' position, i.e. there is zero attenuation. Voltages above 1000mV are still fed into the impedance transformer, but are now reduced by a factor of 1000 since the primary attenuator has been moved into its 'divide by 1000' position. The input to the main amplifier is therefore still only in millivolts.

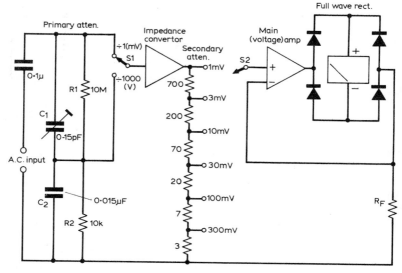

Fig. 2.12   Primary and secondary attenuator circuit.

The primary and secondary attenuators can either be separate, as in Fig. 2.12, in which case separate switching actions will have to be performed, or can be mechanically linked together so that only one control has to be adjusted to obtain any setting between the maximum sensitivity of 1mV, and the maximum input of 300 volts.

**Stray Capacitance**

All components in a circuit possess the property of 'capacitance', either to each other, or to the chassis, the cabinet, or whatever is around them. This property is not normally a desirable one, and can often be a source of great trouble. In this application, the capacitance of R1 and R2 to earth (cabinet, chassis etc) can upset the attenuation afforded by them, the error increasing with increasing frequency, remembering that the reactance of a capacitor is inversely proportional to the frequency.

In order to provide a truly aperiodic attenuator, i.e. one that is not frequency conscious, it is essential to compensate for the effects of stray capacitances around R1 and R2. Since it is not practicable to calculate these strays with any pretensions to accuracy, it is common practice to provide, deliberately, a large and predictable 'lump' capacitance across R2. R1 can then have a suitable capacitor connected across it, and this is normally a variable or trimmer capacitor with a capacitance inversely proportional to the resistance ratio.

In Fig. 2.12, the capacitors are C1 and C2, with valves of 15nF and 15pF. C1 is adjusted by first feeding in a signal at around 1000Hz, upon which it will have no effect, such that a given deflection is obtained upon the meter. The frequency is then increased as much as possible, and to not less than 10kHz, and C1 is then adjusted to give the same deflection.

The primary attenuator must, of course, be in its 'divide by 1000' position, and the generator used *must* have a level output between the upper and lower frequencies. In theory, the attenuation is truly aperiodic when the time constant of R1 times C1 is equal to that of R2 times C2, and since C1 is adjustable, it is to be hoped—if not actually expected—that all strays are properly accounted for.

## Impedance Transformer

The resistors comprising the secondary attenuator are sufficiently low in value not to require frequency compensation, so that the only other factors affecting the overall frequency response of the complete instrument are the impedance transformer and the main amplifier. With reasonably good design and construction, a substantially flat response from some 20 or 30Hz to at least 100kHz should be obtained with comparative ease, while commercial instruments are available with good levels of accuracy to around 2 or 3MHz, with a still reasonable accuracy to around 4 or 5MHz.

An impedance transformer must present, ideally, an infinite input impedance to the circuit being investigated, and a zero output impedance to the moving coil meter, or whatever it is feeding into. These ideals could be approached very closely in the days of 'vacuum state' devices, otherwise known to the cognocentii as 'bottles'. The advent of the transistor, a current operated device, and hence having a low input impedance, presented problems which were partially solved by single stage circuits with feedback from output to input in a positive direction, but not at a level to cause instability, a technique known commonly as 'bootstrapping'.

Fig. 2.13 shows a single transistor stage where bootstrapping is by means of C2. R1 and R2 comprise the normal thermally stable biasing network, with R3 separating the base of the transistor from the junction of R1 and R2. Since the base of a transistor is in phase with its emitter, the signal fed back by C2 causes the junction of

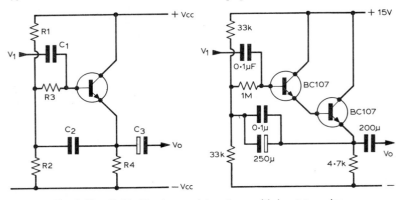

Fig. 2.13    (left)  Single transistor stage with bootstrapping.

Fig. 2.14    (right)  More sophisticated version of Fig. 2.13.

R1, R2, and R3, to move up and down with the emitter voltage. Since both ends of R3 are moving in phase, with the emitter voltage somewhat less than the base voltage, it will 'appear' to have a resistance value very much larger than it really is. What has happened is that the *a.c. impedance* of R3 has been amplified by the current gain of the transistor. Using this technique, input impedances around 500kΩ are possible, and may suffice for some non-critical uses.

In practice, it is normal to use more sophisticated circuits, since the increase in cost is less than the increase in performance. A good practical example is illustrated in Fig. 2.14. The 'gain' of this circuit is a little less than unity, but the input impedance is several Megohms, with a bandwidth extending to several MHz, certainly more than adequate for audio frequency work. Component values are shown, as are transistor types, as this is a most useful circuit in its own right.

Circuits using bi-polar transistors have been designed to provide input impedances of several thousands of Megohms, but as they are of very limited bandwidth, are of academic interest only, so far as we are concerned any way!

**FET Source Follower**

For audio frequency use, an FET arranged as a source follower can be used, and even simple circuits are capable of providing several Megohms input impedance, the gate resistor being the controlling factor, with low input capacitance, and low output resistance. The source follower, like its thermionic counterpart, the cathode follower, has a voltage 'gain' less than unity, typically 0·7 to 0·9. With suitable bootstrapping, the input impedance can be increased even further, and the FET would appear to be the ideal input device.

Unfortunately, it is nowhere near as robust a device as a thermionic valve, or the bi-polar transistor even, and can be all too easily damaged by overloads. Careful circuit design, followed—hopefully! —by careful usage, can ensure that the FET will be a viable input device. A common form of protection used is a pair of very low leakage silicon diodes connected in reverse across the input to the FET, and preceded by a current limiting resistance/capacitance combination. The essentials are shown in Fig. 2.15a.

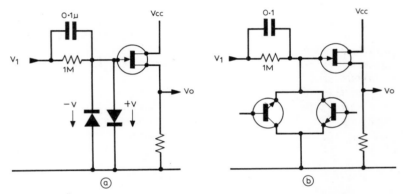

Fig. 2.15 (a) Source protection of FET input device, (b) Alternative form of protection.

An alternative form of protection shown in Fig. 2.15b is a pair of p-n-p/n-p-n transistors which replace the diodes. The theory behind the circuits is that an excessive input, of either polarity, that exceeds the breakdown voltages of the diodes, or transistors, is safely bypassed to chassis, the RC combination limiting the current that can be drawn. In both cases, the FET is protected from excessive voltage inputs.

Since the impedance transformer is at the very front of the circuit, it must be designed to have a very low level of self generated noise, as any noise here will tend to vitiate low level readings. Fortunately, modern transistors and circuit design have combined to provide very low levels of self generated noise, and figures of less than 1% of f.s.d. on the most sensitive range, with the input shortcircuited, should be obtained.

**Main Amplifier Gain**

The gain the main amplifier has to provide is dependent on the maximum sensitivity the instrument is to have, and upon the f.s.d, requirements of the meter movement. It is common practice to provide the amplifier with a little more gain than is actually required. and then to reduce the gain by means of a preset control so that the meter indicates some precise, predetermined, voltage.

It is possible to provide adequate gain for modest requirements by means of a single transistor, but it is more common to utilise at least two transistors, and usually three are used to provide a large amount of surplus gain. Negative feedback can then be applied to reduce the gain to the exact amount required, ensuring stability, good linearity and an adequate frequency response.

Fig. 2.16 shows a fairly simple circuit, but one possessing all the requirements of a reliable design. Three transistors are used in a direct coupled ring-of-three configuration. The direct coupling ensures a good low frequency response, free from phase shift problems. D.C. stability is ensured by the negative feedback from Tr3 collector to Tr1 base, via the 100kΩ and 250kΩ resistors. The 47μF capacitor decouples all a.c. signals, leaving only d.c. feedback. The 250kΩ preset is adjusted to provide a current in Tr3 collector of 2mA to ensure ample current to drive the 50μA meter.

A.C. feedback from the collector of Tr3 to the emitter of Tr2

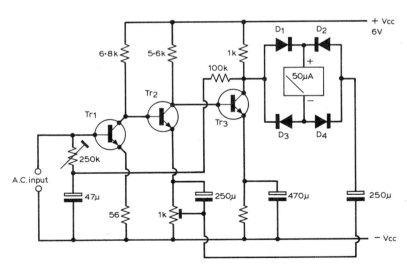

Fig. 2.16   Simple circuit design for 3-transistor main amplifier.

contains the meter and rectifiers, and ensures good linearity, the 1kΩ preset being adjusted for the gain required, typically 1mV for f.s.d. This is a most useful circuit, and so component values are shown; the transistors can be any low current silicon types, the rectifiers being low voltage germanium types.

An alternative circuit giving a comparable performance is shown in Fig. 2.17. This is capable of being developed into a much more refined circuit, providing better linearity and stability.

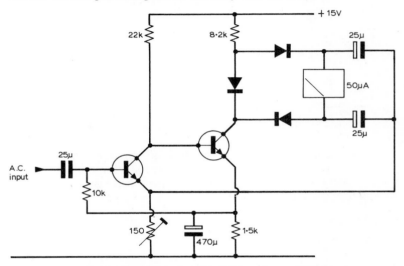

Fig. 2.17   Alternative circuit for main amplifier.

## IC Voltmeter

Just as an 1C can be used for measuring d.c. voltages, so can it also be used for the measurement of a.c. voltages, and via suitable shunts, alternating currents. Fig. 2.18 shows the well known '709' used as a sensitive a.c. voltmeter. With the components shown, the sensitivity is 10mV for f.s.d., at a band-width extending to 100kHz. The gain is dependent on the value of the feedback resistor Rf; altering this will alter the gain, and provide alternative sensitivities. Preceded by a suitable attenuator and impedance convertor, this circuit can form the basis of a most useful millivolt and volt meter.

'Ordinary' multimeters depend on transformers for alternating current measurements, resulting in a greatly reduced frequency range. Electronic meters can insert resistances into circuits for

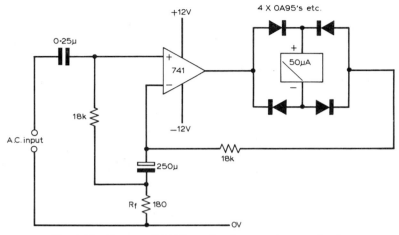

Fig. 2.18   The type 741 IC used as in a.c. voltmeter circuit.

current measurements, and scale the meter in terms of the volts dropped across these resistances as currents. Not only does this method increase the frequency response, but also makes it possible to measure currents too low for transformer-coupled multimeters.

## Combined Electronic Meters

Many designers of test instruments, and users too, follow the philosophy that each instrument can only give of its ultimate performance if designed as a complete entity, and it is therefore common to find separate instruments for the measurement of a.c. voltage and/or current, with another for d.c. voltage and/or current. Design philosophy apart, there are other very important reasons for separate instruments, as explained in Chapter 1, namely that any one instrument can only do one job at a time, be in one place at a time. And since we often want to make a.c. and d.c. measurements simultaneously, there is yet another reason for preferring separate instruments.

Cost often decrees otherwise, and some very good combined instruments are available, often with resistance ranges included, the result of enlightened thinking. These are, in effect, the electronic counterparts of the ubiquitous multimeters, and a very good example is the Avo model EA113. This provides 11 d.c. voltage ranges at 1MΩ/V up to a maximum of 1kV; 8 d.c. current ranges up to

3 amps; 11 a.c. voltage ranges up to 1kV at an input resistance of 10MΩ on the mV ranges; 7 ranges of a.c. current up to 3 amps; and 5 ranges of resistance up to 100MΩ.

Fig. 2.19   The Avo EA113 electronic Avometer.

A somewhat less expensive instrument is the Linstead M2B electronic voltmeter, and the facilities on this are, understandably, less extensive. It is also possible to get a good electronic multimeter in kit form from Heath (Gloucester) Ltd, this being their model IM-104, a comprehensive and compact instrument.

## Choosing an Electronic Multimeter

Many of the remarks made about choosing multimeters in Chapter 1 are equally applicable to electronic multimeters. There are also obvious differences and it is essential to consider these in some detail.

D.C. voltage/current meters, having an amplifier, are susceptible to some degree of drift, and the amount must be very closely controlled if the instrument is to have any pretensions to accuracy and reliability. This is particularly important at the highest sensitivity end where the degree of drift can amount to a significant proportion of the f.s.d., and may completely vitiate any readings made. Most manufacturers indicate to a greater or lesser extent the amount their instruments will drift in a given time and/or temperature changes. There are some instruments with outstandingly good drift characteristics, and these do not have an electronic set zero control for the amplifier.

The gain of the amplifier must also be very closely controlled so as not to cause errors. A well designed transistor amplifier should be completely gain stable. Heavy negative feedback can counteract the loss of emission in valves until almost the very end, and it is interesting to note that one of this country's, indeed the world's, most respected manufacturers, Marconi Instruments, still use valves in their TF2604 electronic voltmeter, an instrument covering seven a.c. voltage ranges from 300mV f.s.d. to 1kV f.s.d.

**Battery/Mains Operation**

Freedom from the 'mains' is a feature of transistored instruments that is much appreciated by many people, particularly those who are obliged to carry them around in the course of their work. Batteries are comparatively expensive, and may be called upon to provide high currents leading to a short life. Replacements, if the instrument is used at all extensively, can be an expensive business, and it is as well to remember that most batteries (being apparently psychic!) always seem to fail when no replacements can be purchased! It is therefore worth considering an instrument that will accept rechargeable batteries, or an add-on mains power supply, enabling the mains to be used where available, so extending the life of the batteries.

Some means of indicating the battery voltage is highly desirable, and most commercial meters have a switch facility which enables the battery to be checked *under load*, thus showing *true* battery voltage. Checking the battery *off-load* can be misleading, as a partially discharged battery will give a much higher reading off-load than it will under the proper load.

Input arrangements are of interest, not least because some form of standardisation has yet to be reached, and therefore various connectors are used, each having good and bad points, though the protagonists of each will stoutly deny that their own are in any way bad! Terminals are very convenient to connect to, but are liable to pick up stray hum and r.f. fields, a cause of errors at very low levels, particularly where high impedance circuits are concerned. Screened input connectors are therefore common, varying from the 'co-ax'

Fig. 2.20 The Sugden Si451 millivoltmeter.

connector to the 'BNC' 'PYE' and 'UHF' types. This is a very persuasive argument for purchasing all one's equipment from one manufacturer!

## Desirable Features

Meter scales should be legibly printed, and in the case of a.c./d.c. meters should be provided with a dB scale, allowing rapid plotting of frequency response curves. Range selector switches should be clearly marked, and where several functions are available should be electrically or mechanically inhibited, so that two functions—or more—cannot be selected simultaneously.

Instrument cabinets should be of metal to provide screening, but should be provided with insulated surfaces and insulated feet so that hum loops cannot be set up by adjacent surfaces touching on mains operated instruments. Where battery operation ensures mains isolation, it is still highly desirable for cabinet isolation, for spurious signals can be generated by intermittent and unwanted contacts.

Mains operated instruments should have leads long enough to plug into the nearest mains point without being stretched to breaking point; on the other hand, excessive leads can be mechanically dangerous, as well as a possible source of mains field pickup, and these can so very easily upset low level measurements.

It is possible for the individual so inclined to build instruments that will prove satisfactory for the most stringent work, and Fig. 2.21 shows such an instrument that I built for my own use. It has ranges from 1mV f.s.d. to 400V f.s.d. in a 1-4-10 sequence to suit the meter movement. The *essentials* are as shown in Fig. 2.12 with a response extending within $\frac{1}{4}$dB up to 100kHz.

For d.c. work, I built the instrument shown in Fig. 2.22. This has ranges from 30mV f.s.d. to 30V f.s.d. at 1MΩ/V, the meter movement being the well known BPL B 30V. The top range of 30 volts was found to be adequate for my needs at that time.

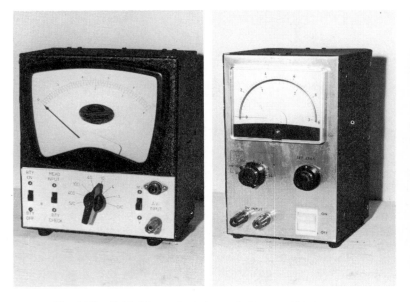

Fig. 2.21   (left)   The author's home-built a.c. millivoltmeter.

Fig. 2.22   (right)   The author's home-built d.c. millivoltmeter.

## Using Electronic Multimeters

Electronic multimeters having built-in power supplies require them to be carefully designed and screened from the rest of the circuit. This is because the mains frequency, and its harmonics, is exceptionally adept at insinuating its way into the signals being 'processed' and causing havoc, not to mention errors! This is particularly applicable to a.c./d.c. meters, where the mains frequency and its harmonics can not only 'blanket' out the desired signal, but can also cause some quite bewildering effects by 'summing and differencing'.

A very simple way of checking for mains-induced troubles in such a meter is to feed in a signal from a battery driven oscillator—so that it cannot introduce its own errors—and then to set it to just above, and below, the mains frequency and its harmonics. If there are any mains-induced leakages, the meter's pointer will 'float' to and fro at the difference frequency. The cure is much less easy!

With battery operated instruments, the battery voltage should be checked, as a matter of course, every time the instrument is used, and the batteries changed as soon as the voltage drops below the permissible level. Exhausted batteries should never be left in an instrument as the effluent, being corrosive, will soon cause some expensive damage. All my own batteries— in accordance with my 'belt, braces, and piece of string' philosophy—are enclosed in plastics bags, the contents of which are regularly checked.

## Earth Loops

Where one, or more, of the instruments in a test are mains operated, it is common practice to remove all earths except one, and then to rely on this for all earthing. This will often prevent the formation of an earth loop, wherein the minute differences in resistance of the different 'earths' can result in a p.d. being set up across one or more of them, this p.d. then possibly vitiating the readings obtained. For this reason, also, it is a good plan to try the effects of different earthing configurations; by doing so it is often possible to significantly reduce the magnitude of the unwanted, mains induced, signal.

Mains transformers, particularly those that are run at, or near, saturation point, generate an appreciable magnetic field, and this may affect sensitive instruments. If this is suspected, moving the (suspect) instrument will also affect its influence, and it should be possible to remove it sufficiently far from the instrument it is affecting or to re-site the suspect instrument such that its field—which will be polarised in a particular direction—is reduced or completely eliminated.

Wherever possible, the electronic meter should be periodically checked, preferably against a proper standard. If this is not possible, a *very rough check* is to compare it against another instrument. This is clearly a doubtful procedure, since we are comparing two unknown instruments against each other, and *possibly* neither is correct, but it *is* a *rough check* and possibly better than no check at all.

As with ordinary multimeters, any overloading must be followed by a proper check, unless the evidence is obviously there in the form of a bent pointer!

## Digital Multimeters

All the instruments we have so far looked at have had pointers which indicated the quantity being measured on a scale, and these are collectively known as analogue instruments. There is another class of instrument, performing *basically* the same functions but operating on quite different principles, and are, in general very much more accurate than their analogue counterparts. These utilise various kinds of light emitting devices; neon tubes were originally used—and still are where large—typically 0·6″—character heights are required.

In the majority of new instruments, except possibly the very cheap ones, neon tubes have been largely supplanted by incandescent filament devices, or by light emitting diodes, principally because they are easy to interface with the semiconductor devices that form the 'works' of the meters, but also because they do not require the 150 or so volts that neon tubes require for their operation.

Like many principles, the principle of digital meters is essentially simple; the problems—and cost—arise when the principles have to be translated into practice. In essence, then, the d.c. voltage or current to be measured is compared with an internal voltage standard, the p.d. across a capacitor, within a given time, being a measure of the input voltage. Fig. 2.23 shows the essential of the so called dual-ramp system that is the basis of most DMM's.

At the commencement of the measurement cycles, C1 is discharged. The input to the integrator is connected to the unknown voltage, causing C1 to commence charging, the rate of charge depending on the input voltage and R1, and this continues until the counter has reached 2000, or 20mS, at which point the voltage across C1 is

$$E = \frac{Vi\ Tl}{RC}$$

The input to the integrator is then switched to the reference voltage and C1 begins to discharge at a rate dependent on the reference voltage and R1. As the reference voltage, Vr, is greater than the input voltage Vi, C1 discharges more quickly than it was

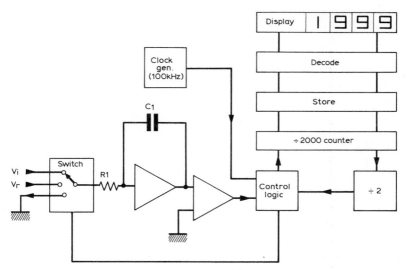

Fig. 2.23 Essential components of dual-ramp system.

charged up, and after a time, T2, will have decayed to zero, this condition being reached when

$$E = \frac{Vr\ T2}{RC} = \frac{Vi\ T1}{RC} - \frac{Vr\ T2}{RC} \text{ or Vi is equal to } \frac{T2}{T1} Vr$$

The discharged condition is then sensed by the comparator which then causes the control logic to switch the input of the integrator to earth, so preventing the charge on C1 changing, simultaneously causing the counter to store the count. The switch shown in Fig. 2.23 is *not* a mechanical switch, but an electronic one which is infinitely faster, and superior to, any mechanical switch. The counter then continues to repeat the cycle.

The basic range of the instrument is dependent on the reference voltage Vr, which is customarily made 200mV and 2V, providing two *basic* ranges of 199mV and 1999mV. Higher voltages are provided for by series range resistors, currents by means of shunt resistors, and a.c. voltage and current is measured after being rectified. Resistances are measured by applying a constant current across them, the resulting volts drop being measured, but displayed as resistance. Much of the front ends of DMM's is not dissimilar to analogue instruments.

An illustration of the added facilities possible is shown in Fig.

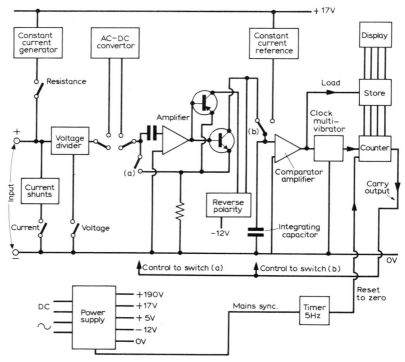

Fig. 2.24   Block diagram of the Advance DMM3 digital voltmeter.

2.24 which shows the block diagram of the Advance DMM3, a very popular instrument.

## Choosing a Digital Multimeter

With an analogue instrument, there is a little room for doubt and for disagreement as to precisely what the pointer is indicating, but the cold, uncompromising stare, of the DMM has an air of absolute and unassailable finality that defies doubt or disagreement, and because of this many people take it at face value; its reading is accepted as Gospel. This is totally wrong. The DMM, like any other instrument has its limitations, and it certainly is not infallible.

All instruments from a reputable manufacturer are provided with a specification that states the limits of permissible error, and what the instrument will, and (just as important) will not, do. The specification of a DMM is the first hurdle to be faced by the prospective purchaster, and even if the manufacturer has been absolutely honest, his specification may still be full of ambiguities.

The DMM should be classified by the number of full digits displayed, as it sometimes is. But if over-ranging is offered—as it often is—then a fraction of a digit is tacked on—$2\frac{1}{2}$ $3\frac{1}{2}$ $4\frac{1}{2}$ and so on. But the fraction has no absolute, universal, interpretation and is dependent on the manufacturers inclinations. Fractions do not tell us what we are interested in, the full scale value and the resolution, and the only reliable way of specifying these is by specifying the maximum count. When this is given, it is possible to arrive at a *theoretical* maximum resolution. With a three digit instrument it is possible to resolve one part in 999, an accuracy of 0·1%. This in turn is dependant on the location of the decimal point, so that whilst the resolution percentage remains unchanged, the resolution in terms of units—volts, amps, ohms,—does not.

## Number of Digits

It is not unreasonable to think that the greater the number of digits in an instrument the more accurate it is; after all we can work to several places of decimals. This is incorrect. The accuracy of a DMM is dependent on the accuracy of its internal voltage (reference) standard, range resistors, amplifiers, analogue/digital convertors, and it is virtually impossible to specify permissible errors in a totally unambiguous way. And whatever method is used to specify 'accuracy', the effects of time, temperature, and humidity have to be allowed for, and many manufacturers specify that their instruments are to 'x%' for a given period of time.

The input resistance of DMM's is traditionally higher than analogue instruments—10MΩ constant as a minimum, extending to 1000MΩ. If we look at Fig. 2.23 again, we can see that R1 follows the input voltage, isolating it from C1. This means, ideally, that R1 must be as high as possible so that when a low impedance voltage is being measured C1 is not 'loaded down', decreasing accuracy. At the same time, the input capacitance will be in parallel with any a.c. being measured, and if this is at all appreciable then its reactance will reduce the resistive input value.

The switching waveforms inside the DMM are difficult to keep inside it, and some older models had almost as much voltage coming *out* as there was going *in*! Modern DMMs are better in this respect, but it is still worth checking on.

It is very easy to become over-enthusiastic when choosing a DMM

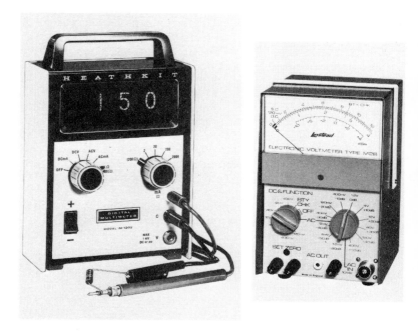

Fig. 2.25 (a) Heathkit IM-1202 digital multimeter, (b) Lonstead M2B electronic voltmeter.

and to go for an instrument that is not absolutely essential. A 4-digit DMM is clearly a greater attraction than a mere 3-digit instrument; 0·01% is clearly more attractive than just 0·1%. Is that extra expense really justified? Have you won the pools? Is your faithful old analogue multimeter no longer good enough? Can you really afford it?

If the answer to all these questions is 'no', then very serious consideration must be given to simpler, less expensive DMMs; they may not impress your visitors as much as a more expensive DMM, but they will do what *you* want them to, and at *your* price. A very good example of such an instrument is the Advance *Alpha*. An inexpensive instrument that can be purchased as a kit of parts is the Heathkit model 1M-1202.

The size of the display can be important, either because of indifferent eyesight or because the DMM must be capable of being read from across the room. Tiny LEDs are adequate for close work, but try reading them from some distance away! The ambient light is yet another important factor, for some displays that are adequate in dim light fade away when subjected to strong light.

## Using Digital Multimeters

The very first thing to do with a new DMM is to thoroughly read its instruction book! This will tell you most of what you must do, and must not do. Surprisingly, perhaps, one of the most important factors requiring regular attention is to the calibration of the instrument. In order to do this, a source of voltage equal to the basic range—usually 1·999 volts—is essential, and the accuracy of this must clearly be better than the anticipated or quoted accuracy of the DMM. The Advance DMM3, for instance calls for an accuracy of 0·1% or better. Such calibration, or at least a check of the calibration, is desirable at intervals of a month.

Most DMMs state that an overload can be applied to any range—250 volts on the 200mV range for instance—and this can give a sense of false security. On a.c. voltage there is an allowance for frequency that should be made, but often isn't. This is sometimes defined as the product of volts × Hertz, and allows the permissible overload for any given frequency to be determined. The product, whatever it may be, divided by the frequency, gives the voltage that can *safely* be impressed into the DMM without damaging it.

Fig. 2.26   Advance digital multimeters DMM2 and DMM3.

If this product is not quoted, it is worth enquiring about if any highish frequencies—and with DMMs this is only around 20 to 30kHz—are likely to be measured, for if the DMM is damaged by such an overload it is very probable that the manufacturer will deny any liability: even if he forgot to mention it in his instruction book!

It is worth checking by means of a sensitive oscilloscope whether the switching waveforms referred to in the previous section are escaping via the *input* terminals. Not only can these vitiate any readings made, but if sensitive semiconductor devices, FETs, MOSFETs and so on, are ostensibly *feeding* the DMM it is possible for these to be damaged.

For a.c., the input signal must be rectified prior to being measured. Many DMMs read either peak or average values, even though they are—ostensibly at least—r.m.s. reading. In common with other peak or average reading instruments, the accuracy is adversely affected when the input signal is not truly sinusoidal, which many signals simply aren't, for we do not always deal with pure sinusoids straight off a low distortion oscillator! The greater the departure of the signal from a true sinusoid, the greater the error in the indicated reading, and if absolute accuracy, or something close to it, is required, it will be necessary to either buy a true r.m.s.-reading DMM, or else stick to pure sinusoidal signals.

### Power Output Meters

For the measurement of power, and here we are concerned specifically with a.c. power, it is customary to measure the a.c. voltage across a load, and then to compute the power by Ohm's law of $E^2/R$. The voltage can be measured by a suitable voltmeter, bearing in mind the remarks made earlier in Chapter 1. about adequate frequency response if using an ordinary multimeter. For this work it is preferable to use an electronic a.c. voltmeter, which also has the great advantage of also allowing very low voltages to be measured, allowing very low power outputs to be computed.

For occasional use, this method is quite satisfactory, but where many such measurements are involved it can become tedious and therefore potentially dangerous, for tedium usually begets errors. The use of a proper power output meter is therefore greatly desirable to facilitate the direct measurement of numerous power readings. Such an instrument is nothing more elaborate than an a.c. voltmeter calibrated directly in terms of watts and milliwatts. Due to our old problem, the square law, the scale of such an instrument is usually non-linear, unless special correction circuitry is used, and this of course pushes the price up. The *essentials* are shown in Fig. 2.27, although individual designs may differ in details.

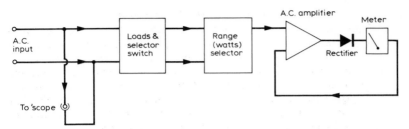

Fig. 2.27 Block diagram of power representative power output meter.

Since the accuracy is dependent upon the precise value of the *load*, as well as for operating convenience, most power output meters incorporate built-in load resistances. For a.f. work, loads corresponding to the standard output impedances of 4, 8, 15Ω are commonly provided, with a 600Ω load being a very useful addition. It is essential that the load resistors are indeed pure d.c. resistances without any reactive components to upset the output stages of any power amplifier that they will be used to load. The fact that the loudspeaker is all reactive is immaterial—even though it may play havoc with an amplifier that is satisfactory with a pure d.c. resistive load!

## Choosing a Power Output Meter

Few amplifiers intended for the domestic market have power outputs in excess of 50 watts (r.m.s.) per channel, and for this type of work, the most common application, a power output meter with a 50 watt f.s.d. will suffice. This, then, is the first decision to be made. With some amplifiers, poor initial design, or the ravages of time affecting component values, will cause the distortion at low power outputs to increase, and this can be subjectively very annoying. The power output meter should, therefore, be capable of measuring low powers accurately in conjunction with a distortion factor meter or wave analyser.

The second decision involves the load resistances available, and these should be at least 4, 8, and 15Ω. The power rating must be consistent with the f.s.d. ratings; it is not uncommon to find two ratings: a continuous rating and an intermittent rating, usually twice the continuous rating for some specified period of time.

The bandwidth must at least equal the audible range of around 20Hz to 20kHz. This is the minimum, and ideally the top range should extend several octaves higher to permit exhaustive testing of amplifiers aspiring to the greatly debased hi-fi label.

Finally, but not necessarily least, accuracy. Remembering that a change in power of only 3dB means that it has changed by a factor of $\times$ 0·5 to $\times$ 2, i.e. half or twice as much, we must aim for an accuracy appreciably better, or we can 'lose' valuable—and expensive—watts by a meter that reads low, or be deluded into thinking we have a super power amplifier by a meter that reads high! The provision of a dB scale greatly facilitates the plotting of frequency response curves. See, however, Chapter 5, attenuators.

## Commercial Power Output Meters

These can be obtained from a number of companies, of which the one by Marconi Instruments, the TF 2500 is a very comprehensive instrument. Again we are faced with the perennial problem of cost versus ones bank balance! Quality plus a comprehensive specification costs a great deal, and it may be necessary to settle for something simpler and cheaper.

With regard to kits, as usual, we come across the Heathkit Co: Their power output meter is the K/AW-1U, a very sensible compromise between cost and specification, and being a well tried design— if a little dated—should prove to be reliable over a very long period of time.

## Home Made Power Output Meters

Here, provided one can circumvent the problem of obtaining, or making—and with a little ingenuity it can be done—accurate, low resistance, high wattage resistors, the individual can build himself an excellent power output meter. Depending upon the *lowest* f.s.d. power required, an a.c. amplifier of the Fig. 2.18 type can be utilised as the basis, the *range* resistors being calculated as outlined in Chapter 5 (L attenuators) with V1 being the input to the range attenuator, and V2 being the output from the attenuator to suit the sensitivity of the a.c. amplifier.

My own power output meter, home made as are almost all my instruments, has resistance ranges of 4, 8, 15 and 600$\Omega$, with f.s.d. ranges of 0·5W, 5W, and 50W. continuous rating. It follows the recipe outlined above and has provision for an oscilloscope to be connected in parallel with the load, an essential requirement since waveform deformation can invalidate any readings made.

## Power: R.M.S. or Continuous?

Because the voltage across a load is measured in r.m.s. terms, then squared and divided by the load i.e. $E^2/R$, it is customary to call the product r.m.s. watts. This is incorrect, since what we are actually getting is continuous power. We can certainly determine r.m.s. power by squaring the *instantaneous* power, integrating to find the power squared mean value and extracting the square root. Like many misconceptions it is now impossible to determine how this situation arose, but we are certainly stuck with it!

# CHAPTER THREE

# AUDIO FREQUENCY OSCILLATORS

---

AN EXPERIENCED ENGINEER, armed with nothing more exotic than a screwdriver with which to 'tickle' the appropriate circuits, can deduce a surprising amount of information about the state of health of a.f. equipment on which he is working. For more accurate, qualitative tests, even he will require something more precise, in the form of an audio signal variable, when required to be, in voltage and frequency.

### The Audible Range

The audible range covers about 20Hz to about—with young children —20kHz, with the passing years taking their toll and reducing the upper limit to around 10kHz to 16kHz in adults. It could be reasonably supposed that an oscillator covering such a range would suffice, but in practice an extension of the upper range by at least an octave is highly desirable. This is because many sounds, principally transients, contain higher order harmonics and the removal of these by an amplifier unable to cope with them will cause that sound to lose its timbre and it will 'sound different'.

In order to *thoroughly* test an amplifying system it is essential to be able to measure its response well above the *nominal* audible range. There is yet another reason. Modern transistor amplifiers use high fт transistors, and heavy doses of negative feedback in order to obtain low distortion levels and precisely tailored responses, a combination which unless expertly handled will result in an amplifier very prone to instability, a condition where it oscillates at some, usually high, frequency either continuously or when provoked by some particular, usually transient, signal.

An artificial transient signal is therefore required, and is provided by the squarewave. This has the property of changing very rapidly from maximum to minimum, and vice versa, with vertical sides and horizontal tops and bottoms. Such a signal will provoke any amplifier with instability tendencies into oscillation, and as such is a most useful signal. It can also, on a suitable oscilloscope, provide an immediate visual display of the characteristics of any a.f. system through which it is passed.

## A.F. Signal Source

In the past, the traditional source of a.f. signals was the beat frequency oscillator, or b.f.o. The *elements* of this are shown in Fig. 3.1. The essentials were a fixed frequency oscillator, f1, usually at 100kHz, and a variable frequency oscillator, f2, the frequency variation of which was dependent on the actual a.f. required. Thus, if a frequency variable from 0 to 20kHz was required, f2 was made variable from 100kHz to 120kHz, and so on. In *principle*, the b.f.o. is an attractive instrument since the whole of the frequency range can be covered in a single range. In *practice*, where it really matters, it has several disadvantages, the major one being the impossibility of obtaining low distortion low frequencies due to the two oscillators 'pulling-in' in spite of screening and buffering.

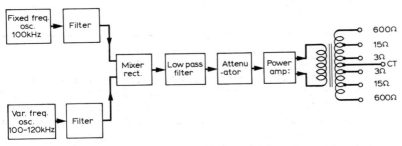

Fig. 3.1   Block diagram of b.f.o.

The frequency determining network enjoying the greatest popularity at present is that based on the Wein bridge, shown in Fig. 3.2 and in Fig. 3.3. Here, the output from Tr1—since we have to start somewhere—is amplified and reversed in polarity by Tr2, which in turn feeds back to Tr1 via the Wein network R1, C1, and R2, C2. At a frequency equal to $1/2\pi\sqrt{R1\,C1\,R2\,C2}$ the signal across R2, C2 is in phase with that across the whole network but $\frac{1}{3}$ as great. The voltage at the base of Tr1 is therefore 180° out of phase with the collector voltage, and provided the overall gain of Tr1 and Tr2

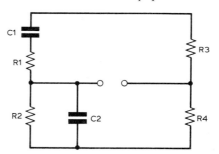

Fig. 3.2    Basic Wein bridge circuit.

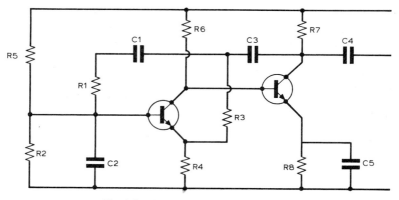

Fig. 3.3    Wein bridge oscillator circuit.

is × 3, to compensate for the network loss, oscillations will result.

This is, of course, a very primitive oscillator, and the output would be grossly distorted. But, by applying our old panacea, negative feedback, to an amplifier having a gain as great as possible, such that the gain is controlled at × 3, we can obtain a relatively pure sine-wave output. In Fig. 3.3, n.f.b. is applied via C3, R3, R4. and from Fig. 3.2 it will be seen that these form, in conjunction with C1, R1, and C2, R2, a bridge, hence the name. This bridge is balanced at a frequency where $R = \frac{1}{2}\pi fc$ assuming all the Rs and Cs are equal, as they usually are.

## Amplitude Stabilisation

However, although we now have a theoretically practicable circuit, in practice it will be found that the gain will vary such that the oscillations cease, or increase to the point where saturation occurs, the output then being a squarewave, which, though on occasions useful, is not quite what we started out in search of. Since it is not practicable to continually vary the feedback manually, for such a task would be highly inconvenient, it is necessary to seek automatic means, and the insertion of thermistors in place of R3 is one such way, another being the insertion of tungsten filament lamps in place of R4.

In both instances, the resistance of the device is dependent on *applied* voltage, and hence on the current flowing *through* it. In the case of thermistors in this application what we want is a *negative* resistance coefficient, i.e. one where the resistance *decreases* with *increasing* current, or increasing applied voltage. Tungsten filament lamps, however, have the opposite temperature coefficient, and so must be placed in the opposite arm of the bridge. The reason for choosing opposite resistance coefficients can be understood when studying Fig. 3.3.

Consider a thermistor, and suppose the output at Tr2 collector rises. This results in a voltage *rise* across R3 (the thermistor, remember) causing the resistance to *decrease* and increasing the feedback applied to Tr1 emitter. Conversely with the tungsten filament lamp in place of R4. Thermistors require much less power than tungsten filament lamps, are not prone to hunting, are very effective amplitude stabilising devices and can control output to a very few %, typically 0·2dB in a well designed circuit.

In practical terms, C1 and C2 are made equal, and R1 and R2 are usually the two variable resistive elements of a ganged rheostat or variable resistor, connected such that the both sections increase, or decrease, simultaneously when the rheostat is rotated. From the formulae given earlier, it is possbile to deduce that the frequency will increase if either R or C is decreased, and in fact this is so, the *increase* in frequency being proportional to the *decrease* in R or C. For economy, it is usual for C to be varied in decade ranges, R then being selected to provide sufficient overlap, and this is usually the maximum spread attempted, although one or two designers do use smaller overlaps, the Sugden Si 453 being a notable inexpensive, but technically excellent, design. As usual, there are more or less valid reasons for all schools of thought.

## Bridge and Parallel T

An alternative form of frequency determining network is the bridge 'T', shown in its elements in Fig. 3.4. The conditions necessary for

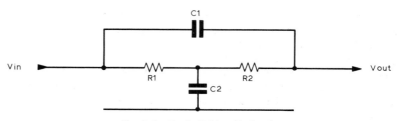

Fig. 3.4   Basic Bridge-T circuit.

specific frequency oscillation are fulfilled when fo $= 1/2\pi RC$ where fo is the frequency in Hz, R is in Ohms, and C is in Farads. All units, it will be seen, are basic. For our particular applications, the formula has to be modified slightly to fo $= 1/2\pi R\sqrt{C1C2}$ since R1 $=$ R2. An excellent oscillator utilising this principle is the Heathkit IG-18, in which ingenious switching results in a true decade oscillator in which the frequency is set not by a variable resistor, but by switches selecting close-tolerance resistors and capacitors to provide a range of 1Hz to 100kHz as shown in Fig. 3.5. Lamp stabilisation is used.

A similar frequency determining network is the parallel T, shown in its essentials in Fig. 3.6. Here both Cs are equal as are both Rs in the series arm. In the shunt arm, the resistance is halved and the capacitance doubled, given very conveniently in practice by connecting the Rs and Cs in parallel. This makes it popular for fixed frequency work; but for continuously variable frequency work it has the disadvantage of requiring a triple gang variable resistor, one— the shunt arm—of which must always be at half the resistance of the two series arms.

A notable example of a parallel T network is used in the Marconi Instruments Tf 2100 oscillator; the switching necessary is shown in Fig. 3.7. This covers the range 20Hz to 20kHz in six overlapping ranges continuously variable from 20 to 63Hz and 63Hz to 200Hz up to the 20kHz maximum. Amplitude stabilisation is by thermistor, with an additional thermistor to compensate for temperature variations.


**Attenuation**


So far we have considered ways of generating sinewaves of predictable and reproducible frequency, and of constant amplitude. Whatever the output, it is unlikely to suffice for all applications, and assuming it is large enough to start with, it will require some means

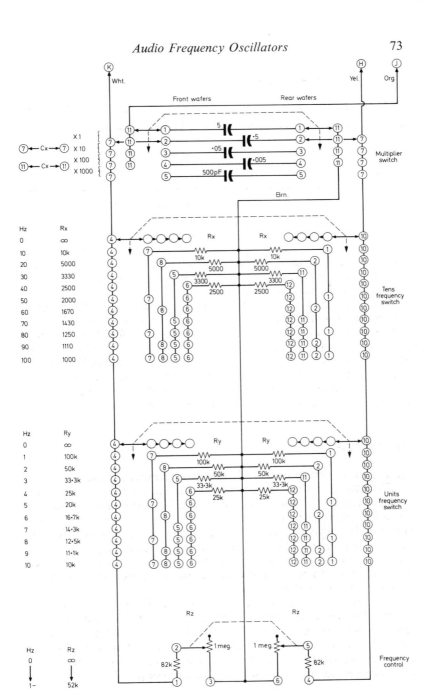

Fig. 3.5  Switching (Bridge-T) of Heathkit notch filter.

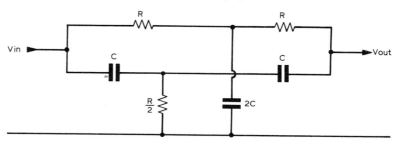

Fig. 3.6    Basic Parallel-T circuit.

of reduction. The easiest way is by means of a potentiometer, somewhat like a radio volume control, and this will suffice for all non-critical applications. For more precise work, a properly designed attenuator must be used—see Chapter 5.

The simplest of these is the potential divider type which offers a number of steps—usually decade—of attenuation, as shown in Fig. 3.8a. It is usual to include a potentiometer for 'filling-in' the gaps between the steps, and this leads to the circuit of Fig. 3.8b. Such an attenuator can be reasonably accurate when feeding into a high impedance load, but low impedance loads can affect the accuracy. For this reason, and because it allows for *proper* loading, the 'T' or 'π' attenuator is preferred—again see Chapter 5.

**Power Supply**

Ideally, an a.f. oscillator should be battery operated, for, as explained in Chapter 2, mains operation requires very careful design and construction if the mains frequency, and its harmonics, are not to insinuate themselves into the required signal. However, where appreciable power is required, batteries are not a really viable proposition, being both bulky and heavy if adequately rated, and most a.f. oscillators come with mains operation as an alternative, the Sugden Si 453 being an exception and using four series/parallel-connected 9 volt batteries.

The output of an oscillator, if properly designed, is *substantially* independent of supply voltage within limits, but it is customary to ensure some degree of voltage stabilisation, from a simple parallel Zener diode, to emitter follower, to compound stabilisation circuits. With mains operation, it is vitally important to ensure that the supply contains the smallest amount of residual ripple possible.

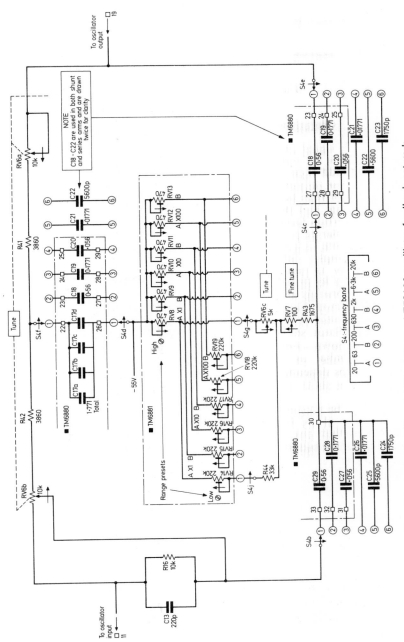

Fig. 3.7  Switching (Parallel-T) of Marconi TF2100 oscillator feedback network.

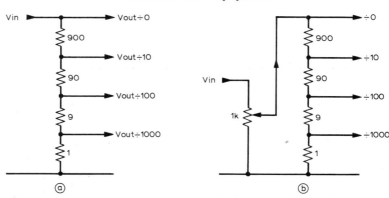

Fig. 3.8　Simple ladder attenuators.

## Output Considerations

The purest signal of which any oscillator is capable is that taken straight from its output, since any intervening *active* devices will inevitably add their own brand of distortion, however small, onto the oscillator output. Without an intervening and isolating device, the oscillator then becomes liable to loading by the load into which it is working, and this may affect the frequency, the output level, or the distortion level. A resistor equal to the lowest load the oscillator will tolerate is sometimes used as an isolating device, but it is more common to use at least a simple emitter follower.

More complex output stages are required, particularly if appreciable *power* is required, and completely isolated, and balanced, outputs may be provided by means of a transformer. This can also be used to provide any number of output impedances, cost being the deciding factor. Due to internal losses, the transformer can only handle a limited range of frequencies, typically 20Hz to 20kHz.

The oscillator should also provide a source of squarewaves. It has been shown—Fourier analysis—that a squarewave contains an infinite number of odd harmonics, their amplitudes and phase relationships depending largely upon the rise time of the transient. We have, in short, a fundamental frequency sinewave and its odd harmonics.

It would be reasonable to suppose therefore that a squarewave is useful only at its fundamental frequency and above; it can be calculated that any amplifier must respond to at least the 20th harmonic if the squarewave is not to be degraded. It is also extremely useful at frequencies lower than its fundamental, for any effect the amplifier may have on the squarewave's phase relationships will be readily shown up on an oscilloscope.

Briefly, the verticals are affected by poor high frequency response, and the horizontals by poor low frequency response, since the time taken by the amplifier to respond to a very rapid change in voltage level—corresponding to a musical transient—is a measure of its high frequency response, while the time allowed by the amplifier for the horizontal portions to settle is a measure of its low frequency response.

## Squaring Circuits

Squarewaves can be provided by a number of circuits fed from the sinewave oscillator, and the simplest of these are a pair of reverse-connected diodes as shown in Fig. 3.9a. Here, use is made of the diode's conduction characteristics above a certain voltage, around 150mV for germanium and around 600mV for silicon. The resistor acts as a current limiter, and the output will be the sum of the two diode's individual voltages, i.e. 300mV p-p and 1200mV p-p. If the diodes are heavily saturated, the output is a reasonable squarewave, but this implies considerable power. This, together with the restricted output, limits the usefulness of this circuit.

An alternative is to overdrive a transistor, and this can be quite effective provided the transistor is driven hard into saturation so that it alternatively cuts-off and bottoms (Fig. 3.9b). The output is then a squarewave with an amplitude that varies from virtually Vcc—being limited only by $I_{ceo}$—and the supply positive—being limited by $V_{cesat}$. The 4·7 kΩ preset resistor in the collector allows any portion of the output between the maximum of $\simeq$ 6 volts p-p and minimum to be selected. If the oscillator output is around the very common 1 volt level, a preamplifier may be required to raise the voltage to a level where full saturation of the transistor occurs.

## Schmitt Trigger

The most popular squaring circuit utilises a regenerative circuit of the bistable type, commonly known as the Schmitt trigger shown in Fig. 3.9c. The state of this circuit, i.e. which transistor is conducting and which cut-off, depends upon the input voltage. Since we have to start somewhere, let us suppose Tr1 is cut-off. The base voltage of Tr2 is then dependent on the potential divider action of R1, R2 and

R3 and will be 6·8 volts. The emitters, connecting to a common emitter resistor R4 will be at 6·6 volts due to the emitter current of Tr2.

As long as the input voltage remains below the emitter voltage, the circuit will remain stable. As the input voltage approaches 6·6 volts, a point is reached when Tr1 begins to conduct, and, due to the regenerative action of the circuit, the states suddenly change, Tr2 is cut-off, and Tr1 is conducting. As long as the input voltage remains above the level necessary for initial triggering, the second state will prevail, hence the bistable bit.

If the input voltage is now reduced, a point will be reached when the transistors revert back to the original state. However, the two triggering voltages are not quite the same, and the difference is known as the hysteresis or backlash of the circuit. The hysteresis is dependent on the loop gain of the circuit, and only disappears when the loop gain is just equal to one. The output voltage is essentially independent of the input voltage, provided this is above a certain minimum.

The frequency of the output is unchanged, and is the same as the input. In a well designed trigger the rise and decay times should be not less than $0.5\mu S$, and there should be no sag of the horizontals, i.e. the wave really is square.

**Choosing A.F. Oscillators**

To be certain that one is not over-specifying (for extra performance costs extra) or under-specifying (resulting in a possibly useless instrument), it is essential to list the duties of the oscillators, i.e. servicing or design/development.

Servicing implies a certain amount of portability, and this in turn implies battery, or mains/battery, or rechargeable battery, operation. Broadly speaking, servicing requires an oscillator with a relaxed specification in terms of distortion and frequency/voltage calibration. If, however, servicing on proper hi-fi equipment, to original standards, is intended, then quite clearly the oscillator must be up to the specification of the instruments used by the hi-fi equipment manufacturer.

Pure design, or design/development, requires an oscillator built to a much more stringent specification, with minimal distortion, and with frequency/voltage calibrations to a high order of accuracy. Ideally, the distortion level of an oscillator should not exceed $\frac{1}{10}$ of the distortion expected in the equipment under test, and this is rarely over 0·1%, requiring an oscillator distortion of 0·01%. Also

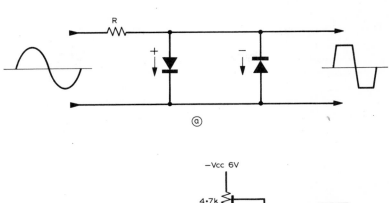

(a)

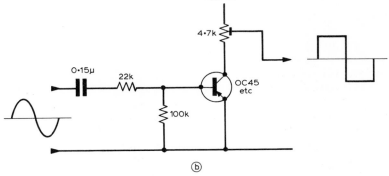

(b)

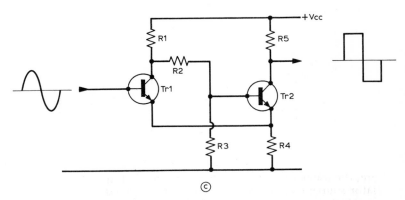

(c)

Fig. 3.9 Squaring circuits.

ideally, this level should not be exceeded over the range of 20Hz to 20kHz, though sometimes this is the required level mid-band (1kHz) with a relaxed specification, say 0·05%, over the rest of the frequency range.

Both frequency and voltage should be accurate, certainly within 3% at worst, initially, and the repeatability should also be within these limits, including warm-up time where applicable. Short term frequency drift can be important when making distortion tests, as it can be very infuriating to set up the distortion factor meter, only to find that the oscillator has drifted. Drift, expressed as a percentage should not exceed 1% in a well designed oscillator.

**Effect of Load**

The voltage output can be affected by the load into which the oscillator is working, even though the attenuator/s *may* be set to a *specific* voltage output. Some oscillators are provided with an internal voltmeter and this usually indicates the *input* to the attenuator, so that the (loaded) output voltage may bear little relationship to the input voltage. The problem here is one of e.m.f. and p.d., and upon which of these the attenuator or voltmeter is scaled. Although e.m.f. and p.d. problems are more applicable to r.f. oscillators, they are possible sources of trouble for us here, and so it is as well to consider their implications now, and Fig. 3.10 shows the essentials.

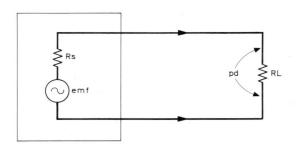

Fig. 3.10　Signal generator e.m.f. and p.d.

Here, the oscillator output is shown as an e.m.f. in series with the oscillator source resistance, Rs, working into a load resistance, $R_L$, across which the p.d. is developed. If the attenuator is calibrated in terms of e.m.f., it means that the source resistance appears in series with the oscillator voltage (e.m.f.). The p.d. developed across the load is thus dependent upon the resistance of that load, being 50% of the e.m.f. when, and only when, the source and load resistances are equal.

If the load resistance is very high, then there will be very little voltage 'lost' across the source resistance, and the p.d. will virtually equal the e.m.f. If, however, the load resistance is less than the source resistance, the voltage dropped across it will be greater than 50%, and so the e.m.f. will be greater than the p.d. In practical

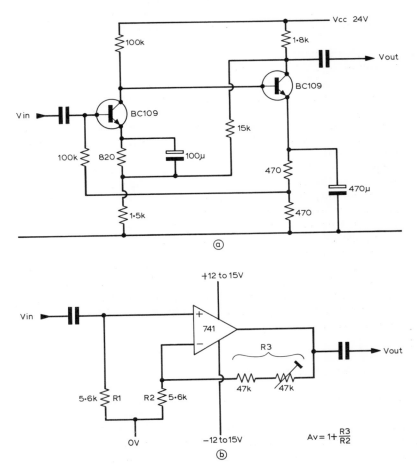

Fig. 3.11 Typical x10 amplifier circuits.

terms, there is no difference, the difference being one of terminology only, but it is clearly essential to fully understand the implications of e.m.f. and p.d. calibrations.

## Oscillator Output

The oscillator should, ideally, have an output of at least 10 volts r.m.s., permitting tests to be effected on virtually all types of a.f. equipment. However, the output of many oscillators is less, at around a volt or so, and this can limit the tests that can be successfully effected. If minimal distortion is not essential, then a simple add-on amplifier can be very easily constructed as shown in Fig. 3.11a and 3.11b. Both circuits have a gain of $\times$ 10, and are intended for a maximum input of 1 volt r.m.s.

The bandwidth of Fig. 3.11a is somewhat restricted at the high frequency end, being around 20kH$_2$ for the $-3$dB point. However, it is possible to extend this a little by splitting the feedback resistor into two resistors of 7·5k$\Omega$ each, and decoupling the centre point by a capacitor to earth; the capacitor value will have to be found experimentally.

Fig. 3.11b, on the other hand, has a top frequency response extending to 100kHz; the response of either circuit, if built, should be very carefully checked as any little peaks or troughs in the response can quite easily invalidate the response of the oscillator itself. It need hardly be said that neither amplifier must be incorporated into the oscillator itself, for such an act of vandalism will make the manufacturer tear up his guarantee!

The output voltage should ideally be flat within 0·1dB over the bandwidth of interest, although for non-critical applications some relaxation can be permitted, and the amount of relaxation can only be determined by the application, an appropriate correction factor being applied as necessary.

## Commercial A.F. Oscillators

It is possible to obtain an excellent a.f. oscillator—the Sugden Si453 —for around £45, with more complex and expensive instruments available from Advance Electronics and Marconi Instruments, to name but two well known firms. Lyons Instruments make an excellent a.f. oscillator, the type SQ10, with some interesting circuitry. For portability, with a reduced specification, there is the Nombrex model 40 at around £30, and this is probably unbeatable for this application.

Probably the ultimate oscillator is the Radford Low Distortion Oscillator with a distortion figure of 0·002% at 1kHz, increasing to 0·005% from 200Hz to 20kHz. Interestingly, this is a hybrid design, utilising both valves and transistors. It is also expensive!

## Home Made Oscillators

The experienced individual can build an oscillator that will suffice for all but the most exacting requirements. Fig. 3.12 shows such an

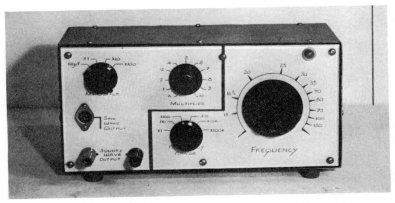

Fig. 3.12    Author's home-built a.f. oscillator, covering 15Hz to 1·5MHz.

instrument that I built several years ago for my own use, and this is used almost daily. It was described in *Practical Wireless* for May 1971. The circuit is shown in Fig. 3.13, and covers the range 15Hz to 1·5MHz, with a distortion below 0·05% between some 40Hz and 20kHz, by careful selection of components and circuit operating levels. The emitter follower, necessary for a low output impedance, regrettably adds its own brand of distortion onto the signal passing through it. The attenuator has a characteristic impedance of 600Ω, the maximum output level being 1 volt r.m.s.

## Using A.F. Oscillators

Like other instruments, use of an a.f. oscillator requires knowledge allied to common sense; the rules are fortunately few. Unlike a

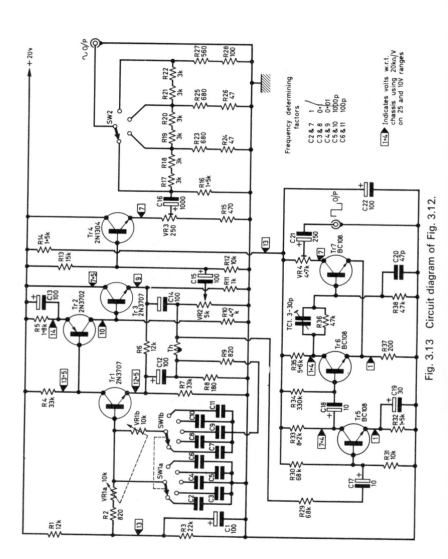

Fig. 3.13 Circuit diagram of Fig. 3.12.

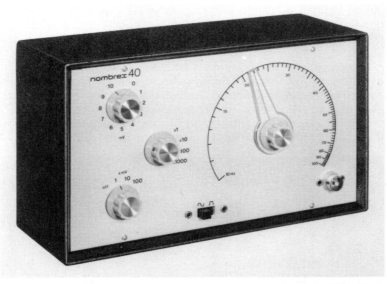

Fig. 3.14   (a) Nombrex type 40 oscillator, (b) Lyons Instruments type SQ10 oscillator.

voltmeter, when you start off on the highest voltage range when in doubt, with an oscillator it is prudent to start off with the output turned right down when in doubt, or else you are likely to have a misfortune, such as having an indignant 'speaker cone come flying at you!

If the oscillator is battery operated, the voltage must be checked each time the oscillator is used, as distortion levels will increase, and voltage levels decrease if the voltage is lower than intended. Mechanically, the state of the batteries should be periodically checked for the reasons outlined in Chapter 2. The oscillator should be switched off when not in use to conserve battery life.

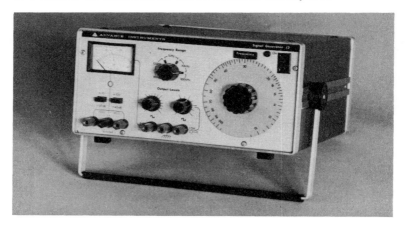

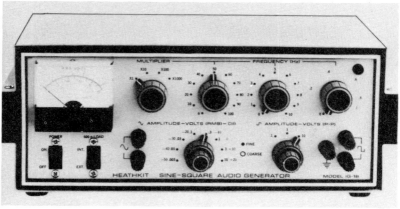

Fig. 3.15  (a) Advance J3 signal generator, (b) Heathkit IG-18 sine-squarewave audio generator.

With mains operated instruments, check the mains voltage tapping before plugging the instrument into the mains socket. At best, you will do no damage, but distortion and voltage levels may suffer if the tapping is incorrectly set. At worst ... The output signal should be periodically inspected to ensure that no filtering degradation has occured, to the detriment of the signal at mains frequency, and its harmonics.

In use, check the earthing arrangements, and try rearranging them; sometimes the improvement in signal-to-noise ratio can be dramatic; sometimes the decrease can be equally dramatic!

It is desirable, essential in the case of oscillators intended for work on equipment of the highest grade, to periodically check the oscillator for distortion levels, frequency accuracy, voltage accuracy. The lower frequencies can be very easily checked by 'beating' them against the mains frequency which is surprisingly accurate; with care and patience, and given a suitable oscilloscope, it should be possible to check up to the tenth harmonic. On the higher ranges, checks can be made by feeding the oscillator signal into a suitable receiver and 'beating' it against the Radio 2 programme on 200kHz.

It is also desirable to periodically measure the oscillator distortion directly, and particularly if really critical measurements have to be made. All circuits deteriorate to some small extent with age and use, and it is bad practice to take any figures for granted.

CHAPTER FOUR

# RADIO FREQUENCY
# OSCILLATORS

---

FOR WORK ON RADIO RECEIVERS of all kinds, it is necessary to have oscillators that will cover the required band of frequencies, commonly from around 150kHz to at least 100MHz for domestic purposes, with an appropriate extension for all other requirements. Just to make matters more interesting, generators covering both f.m. and a.m. are required.

The essentials of r.f. oscillators are fairly simple; the problems arise when they have to be translated into practice! In essence, then, all that an r.f. oscillator has to do is provide signals over a range of frequencies, variable within the required limits, of constant amplitude, of low distortion, with both frequency and amplitude reproducible to close limits.

Traditionally, r.f. oscillators have been categorised as 'service oscillators' and 'standard signal generators', the distinction being that the service oscillator is moderately accurate for frequency calibration, with an output roughly calibrated for amplitude, and variable with the range in use, whereas the standard signal generator is much more accurately calibrated for frequency, with an output amplitude that can be set to precisely determined limits.

The standard signal generator, almost always called a 'sig-gen', sometimes a s.s.g., is frequently used for a moderately accurate frequency source with a very accurate voltage output, the ultimate frequency then being either set by, or compared to, a crystal calibrator.

**Typical Service Oscillator**

Since the service oscillator is essentially simpler than the standard sig-gen, it is more suited for the service technician to whom time is money, and who may not wish, or be able, to afford, a standard sig-gen, which is more time consuming to set up and to use. The block diagram of a typical service oscillator is shown in Fig. 4.1. The very simplest service oscillators consisted of two valves plus a rectifier. One valve functioned as an r.f. oscillator and the other as an a.f. oscillator, the modulation of the r.f. signal being effected by feeding the oscillator valve directly from the a.f. oscillator valve. Current instruments employ virtually the same principles, so that for valves we can read transistors.

In the cheapest and simpler instruments, the output is extracted

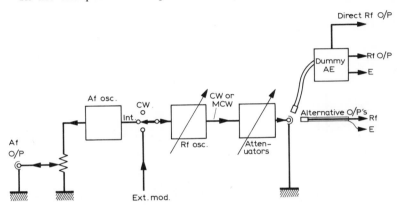

Fig. 4.1  Block diagram of service oscillator.

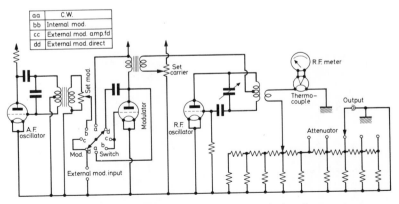

Fig. 4.2  Basic arrangement of Marconi TF144G signal generator.

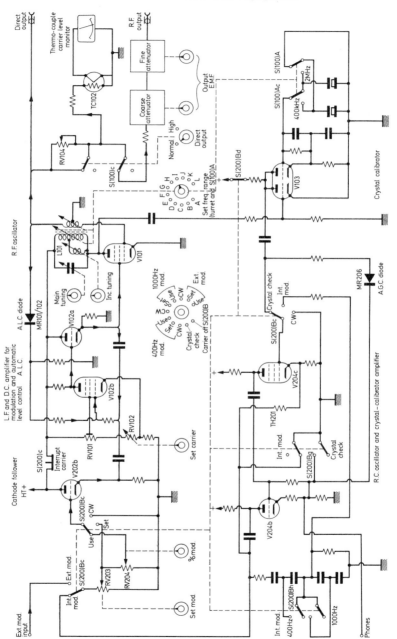

Fig. 4.3 Functional diagram of Marconi TF144H signal generator.

directly from the collector of the oscillator via a 'volume control' type of attenuator, no other intervening device being fitted. Both the oscillator frequency and the voltage are liable to be influenced by the load presented to the oscillator and variations on both will be affected by the setting of the attenuator. Better class instruments derive the output from a coupling winding on the oscillator coils, and these should be somewhat less influenced by the load.

## Signal Generators

Standard sig-gens are much more highly refined versions of service oscillators, and Fig. 4.2 shows the essentials of possibly the most famous model of the post-war years, the Marconi TF144G. This was for several decades, (and almost certainly still is for the impoverished) the mainstay of the r.f. design/development engineer whose interests lay between 85kHz and 25MHz, although versions covering down to 20kHz could be obtained.

Although using valves, this instrument serves to illustrate the principles of r.f. sig-gens, principles which are, of course, equally applicable to modern transistorised instruments. Here, we still have an r.f. oscillator, and an a.f. oscillator, but between the two we have an intermediate modulator valve. We have a coupling to the oscillator coil to extract the output voltage and, very important, we have a thermocouple meter to monitor the oscillator output, so that the attenuator is supplied with a constant r.f. input, ensuring that the output from the attenuator, when properly loaded, is at the required voltage.

Since the efficiency of the r.f. oscillator will, inevitably, vary somewhat from range to range, the 'set-carrier' control permits the h.t. supplied to the oscillator valve to be varied, thus varying the amplitude of the signal, which is monitored by the thermocouple meter, and which is always brought to a predetermined point of the scale by the 'set-carrier' control.

The latest variation of the TF144 is the 'H' series, and this, interestingly, still uses valves! A block diagram of this is shown on Fig. 4.3 from which it will be seen to be more comprehensive—and complex—than its famous predecessor.

## R.F. Oscillators

R.F. oscillators, whether service or sig-gen, fall into three fairly broad classifications, with over-lapping demarcation lines: m.f.

sometimes m.f./h.f. covering up to about 100MHz; v.h.f. covering
up to about 500MHz; and u.h.f. covering up to and over 1000MHz.
As can be imagined, techniques change along the way, and some
quite ingenious solutions to obtaining controlled oscillations have
been developed.

For m.f. work, normal LC techniques can be used, consisting
of resonant tuned circuits, in conjunction with valve or transistor
feedback amplifiers, probably the most popular being the Hartley
configuration. For v.h.f. and u.h.f. work, resonant, or tuned, lines
can be used in place of the tuned LC circuitry. An alternative to
both is used in the Marconi TF995B. Here an oscillator of restricted
frequency coverage (4·5MHz to 13·5MHz) is used with frequencies
above 13·5MHz being obtained by the use of a series of harmonic
multipliers, to provide a top frequency of 202MHz. Frequencies
below 4·5MHz are obtained by heterodyning the output from the
third frequency multiplier with a fixed frequency crystal oscillator
operating at 30MHz.

For a.m. purposes, the r.f. oscillator has to be modulated by an
a.f. signal such that the amplitude of the carrier, i.e. the r.f. signal,
varies in sympathy with the a.f. signal. In the simpler instruments,
this is effected by feeding the r.f. oscillator directly from the a.f.
oscillator such that the d.c. supply has the a.f. signal superimposed
upon it, and since this is effectively in series with the supply voltage,
this will increase and decrease about its mean, or steady state, value
by the amplitude of the modulating signal. The better class instruments modulate the r.f. carrier by means of an intermediate modulating stage, which greatly reduces the amount of f.m. on an allegedly
a.m. signal.

The modulating frequency is usually 400Hz, with 1kHz as an
alternative; the frequency accuracy is not normally important. In
the cheaper instruments, the modulation depth is fixed at the
'normal' level of 30%. For tests on detectors, for distortion, a much
greater depth of modulation is essential, and ideally 100% should be
obtainable. This is difficult to provide without excessive distortion;
the maximum commonly available is around 80%.

**Frequency Modulation**

An alternative to a.m. is f.m. whereby the carrier instead of being
modulated in amplitude is modulated in frequency, so that it varies
above and below its nominal frequency by a rate proportional to
the frequency of the modulating signal, its amplitude remaining
constant. Fig. 4.4 shows the essentials.

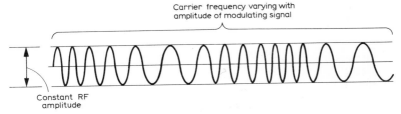

Carrier frequency varying with
amplitude of modulating signal

Constant RF
amplitude

Fig. 4.4   Principle of frequency modulation signal.

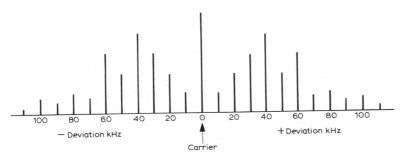

100   80   60   40   20   0   20   40   60   80   100

— Deviation kHz        + Deviation kHz

Carrier

Fig. 4.5   Principles of f.m. sidebands.

The result of frequency modulating a carrier by an a.f. signal is to provide pairs of sidebands at multiples of the modulating frequency as shown in Fig. 4.5. The depth of modulation of a transmitted radio broadcast signal is limited by international agreement as a maximum variation of the nominal frequency for 100% modulation, and this is ±75kHz, i.e. a total swing of 150kHz.

The frequency variation so produced is more properly known as the deviation, and in the example shown corresponds to a 90MHz carrier modulated by a 1kHz signal at 100%, the deviation being from 89·925MHz to 90·075MHz. Reducing the modulating signal by 50% changes the deviation to 89·9625MHz to 90·0375MHz. Summarising, the *carrier deviation* is dependent upon the *amplitude* of the modulating signal, not its frequency.

Modulation techniques for f.m., understandingly, are different than those used for a.m. What is required is a capacitor—or inductor —in parallel with the oscillator tuned circuit that varies in sympathy with the modulating signal. Traditionally, this was effected by a reactance valve, now transistor, circuit. Mechanically, an electric motor could be used driving a capacitor—inconvenient for audio frequency signals! An alternative, and one that I once spent weary hours at, is a modified loudspeaker, with its coil coupled to a capacitance across a tuned circuit, and this at least can be made to work, though the frequency coverage is somewhat restricted.

### Varicap Application

A possibility for use in f.m. oscillators is the Varactor or variable capacitance diode (usually now called a varicap diode), in which the intrinsic capacitance is dependent upon the applied reverse bias. However, since the diode can also be affected by the oscillator voltage, some care in design is required, and a method is to connect two diodes back-to-back. Also, since the capacitance characteristic is essentially non-linear, the deviation possible is restricted. An interesting design, suitable for home construction, appeared in *Wireless World* from August 1970 to October 1970, utilising a varicap as the tuning element.

A method used in the Marconi TF1066B is the ferrite core reactor coupled to the tuned circuit. This is a ferrite core in which the modulating current is superimposed on a fixed current through a saturating coil wound round the coil and forming part of the tuned circuit.

### The Wobbulator

What may be termed a derivative of the frequency modulated oscillator is the wobbulator. Here, an r.f. oscillator is continuously swept over the required band of frequencies synchronously with the timebase of an oscilloscope as shown in Fig. 4.6. The timebase

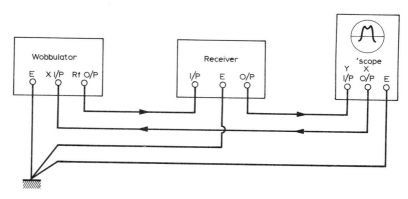

Fig. 4.6   Connections for wobbulator.

output voltage, a sawtooth, is used to control the frequency of the oscillator, providing a proportional relationship between the X deflection and the oscillator frequency.

The tuned circuit of the oscillator has a reactance valve, or transistor, connected across it. The device is connected such that its output impedance is chiefly reactive, and this is controlled by the grid, or base, bias on the device. Changing the bias therefore changes its output reactance, and this in turn changes the oscillator frequency. If the deviation is, say, 30kHz, and the mean frequency is 1MHz, then, with the oscilloscope trace just starting on the lefthand side of the screen, the frequency will be 1MHz–30kHz or 970kHz, increasing as the spot traverses the screen until, in the centre, it will be the mean frequency of 1MHz.

As it continues towards the right hand side, the frequency will continue increasing, until at the end it will be 1MHz + 30kHz or 1·03MHz. Then flyback occurs, and the cycle is repeated. The horizontal, or X scale is therefore a measure of frequency, and the vertical, or Y scale is a measure of voltage. In effect, we are 'drawing' an instant graph, a task that performed manually would be both time-consuming and exceedingly labourious.

Since the oscillator frequency is varying above and below its mean frequency, any lack of symmetry in the receivers—and this can be anything from a simple l.w./m.w. receiver to a complex TV—is immediately shown up, as shown in Fig. 4.7a, b, c. Stagger tuning, a recourse adopted when a wide, flat frequency response is required, is also facilitated by a wobbulator, since individual stages can be aligned individually, the overall response then being displayed for approval or disapproval.

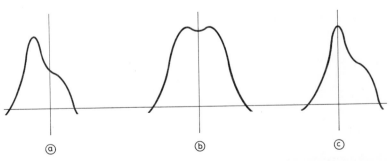

Fig. 4.7 Wobbulator traces: (a) asymmetrical—peaking off mean frequency, (b) symmetrical, (c) asymmetrical—peaking on mean frequency.

## Choosing an R.F. Oscillator

As with a.f. oscillators, the application is essentially design/development or service. A top grade instrument will prove suitable for service, but the reverse is most certainly not true. The probable final arbiter will be the state of ones bank balance, or the temper of ones bank manager! The only possible advice is: buy the very best you can afford; it will reward you with years of reliable service, which some chromium plated importations most certainly will not.

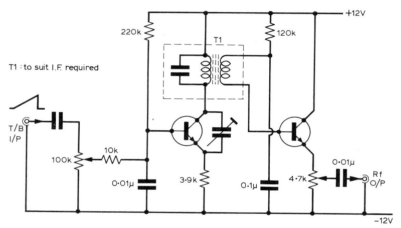

Fig. 4.8   Circuit of typical i.f. wobbulator.

Having decided the task, the next decision is the frequency coverage, and this should be simple; with one very important proviso. All sig-gens worth having are calibrated on *fundamentals*, as they should be; the practice of using *harmonics* is often unreliable since the unwary or the unskilled, and not only the unskilled, can be misled, for I have known expert engineers to be deceived by harmonically calibrated dials, sometimes through pressure of work, sometimes through being owners of poor memories. This is a very personal view, and no doubt there will be dissenters, but it is one that has been arrived at over a very long period of time.

## Frequency Accuracy

The frequency accuracy should be 2% at most, preferably better (at around 1%) and this should include warm up time, drift, and resetting. 1% sounds quite good until you stop and think. At 1MHz, it can mean an error of ±10kHz and pro rata. The f.m. intermediate frequency is 10·7MHz, and at this frequency a 1% error is quite appreciable (±107kHz). Now, neither of these errors may be accounted to be excessive; again they may be. It all depends upon the applied criteria, and on how accurately the operator will want to work.

Resetting accuracy can also be an important parameter, for supposing you change frequency, then change back to the original frequency. How certain can you be that the instrument will deliver its original frequency? Even at ±1%, you can be at the top end or the bottom end of the tolerance spread. Resettability is a function of the drive/coupling/slow motion mechanism used, and my own preference is for a direct calibration with hair line cursor, vide TF144G, rather than for a pointer traversing a scale.

All other factors being equal, the accuracy is only as good as the thickness of the pointer, and if this is deliberately, and with malice aforethought, made thick enough to obscure the calibrations, then where is ones expected 'accuracy'?

In order to improve frequency accuracy, some manufacturers provide an internal crystal oscillator against which the sig-gen can be compared; sometimes the cursor is moveable so that the scale is at all times, if desired, set up against the crystal calibrator. Using such a calibrator, an improvement in calibration accuracy of at least × 10 is possible; with care and skill, × 100 is not impossible. Sig-gens lacking a crystal calibrator can be very easily provided with one, and Fig. 4.9 shows a typical circuit. The 3–30pF trimmer is adjusted to provide the exact frequency required, in comparison with a signal of known accuracy.

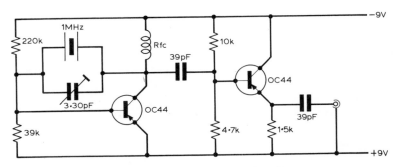

Fig. 4.9   Circuit of 1MHz crystal oscillator.

**Output Voltage**

The output voltage should be closely controllable from less than 1$\mu$V to at least one volt. This allows sensitive receivers to be checked not only for sensitivity (at the $\mu$V level) but also for a.g.c. operation, detector overloading, spurious responses, and general misbehaviour when subjected to an excessive signal, an occurance quite possible in the vicinity of a transmitting station, and this is where the 1 volt level comes in.

The output voltage must be accurate initially, and reproducible subsequentally, and this requires careful design and mechanical construction. Many sig-gens incorporate a thermocouple meter which monitors the voltage *input* to the attenuator allowing this to be set to precisely defined limits. The output is then dependent on two factors: the accuracy of the attenuator—and in a well designed attenuator this is high—and upon the load presented to the attenuator, and this is where, as explained in Chapter 3, we have to resolve e.m.f. and p.d.

Service oscillators are roughly, sometimes very roughly, calibrated for voltage output, and this varies according to the range, and frequency, in use, and is therefore quite unsuited to critical measurements.

In simpler oscillators, operation of the attenuator, sometimes even the inclusion of the load, can significantly alter the oscillator frequency, and this is, clearly, a very undesirable characteristic. In the better class oscillators, more so in sig-gens, the oscillator frequency is unaffected by either the operation of the oscillator or the inclusion of the load. If at all possible, it is desirable to check whether the instrument of one's choice is subject to these defects, before parting with any money, as the validity of any work done is wide open to the greatest suspicion.

**Elimination of F.M.**

Surprisingly as it may seem a.m. oscillators contain some degree of f.m. and vice versa, and this is impossible to eliminate entirely. It is possible to reduce both to negligible proportions, and all sig-gens have the amount of a.m. on f.m. and f.m. on a.m. clearly specified. The Marconi TF801D, for instance, is quoted as being subject to less than 0·001% deviation for a 30% a.m. depth modulation, whilst the Marconi TF1066B is quoted as containing less than 5% a.m. modulation at maximum deviation. Both also specify the figures for carrier modulation, a.m. and f.m. by mains hum and noise, figures which are conspicuously absent on lesser instruments.

## Construction

Standard sig-gens are characterised by a solidity of construction that would not disgrace a battleship, and humping one about is akin to an act of penance! This is not surprising, for any movement of components relative to one another, or to the case, will affect the oscillator frequency (the higher the frequency, the greater the effect) and so great rigidity of construction is very necessary, and recourse to die castings is often made as shown in Fig. 4.10. A good example of solid construction is the Marconi TF144G, which weighed in at some 90lb, and as it cost some £85 when introduced in 1934, gave pound-for-pound value!

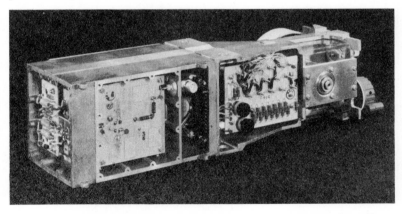

Fig. 4.10   Internal view of Marconi type TF2000, showing one r.f. oscillator unit (a separate oscillator is used for each tuning range).

The voltage should be obtainable only from the authorised outlet, and this clearly requires first class mechanical screening, and also extensive mains filtering in the case of mains operated models, if the signal is not to escape via the back door.

Incremental tuning—essentially bandspreading or 'fine tuning'— by means of a subsidiary control is essential so that the frequency can be varied, over a limited range, above and below that set on the main tuning scale. This permits small frequency adjustments, to a high degree of accuracy, and greatly facilitates the measurement of receiver selectivity.

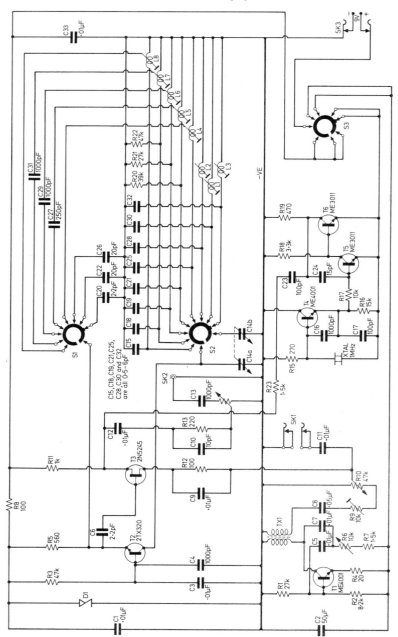

Fig. 4.11   Circuit diagram of Nombrex model 41 r.f. signal generator.

## Commercial R.F. Oscillators and Sig-Gens

It is possible to purchase an r.f. oscillator for around £20 by searching the advertisements pages of the electronics periodicals, and these will suffice for all non-critical purposes where great accuracy cannot be expected. By roughly doubling one's budget, it is possible to obtain an instrument where the frequency scales are more accurate, though it is wise not to place too great a reliance upon the voltage output. Unfortunately, most of these are calibrated on harmonics for the upper frequency ranges.

A good example of this class of instrument is the Eagle SG70. Where portability is essential, the Nombrex range is outstanding. I still have, and occasionally use, one of their model 27 oscillators. The current Nombrex instruments are the model 41 and the model 42; the former has a more comprehensive specification, plus a built-in crystal calibrator. The circuit diagram is shown in Fig. 4.11. Service oscillators are also manufactured by Avo; their current model is the HF 134.

Fig. 4.12   Marconi TF2015 a.m./f.m. signal generator.

Standard sig-gens are available from a number of firms, of which the best known in the UK is Marconi Instruments. Reference has been made to this firm's products from time to time, and the reader will have guessed that I am a TF144G addict. This is quite true. I do not know of any instrument—within its frequency range— that I would prefer; at least, one that I can afford! This brings us to the question of spares, an ever increasing worry in these days of built-in obsolescence.

The TF144G was introduced as long ago as 1934, and continued until 1959, with limited production until the mid-1960's; spares and service are still available from the manufacturer. Not many companies, particularly those that change their models every other year—or sooner—can offer such very good service, and it is a recommendation to purchase your instruments from an established, reputable, manufacturer. They will cost you much more initially, but viewed as a long term investment project, as it ought to be, the extra cost will prove worthwhile.

Current Marconi sig-gens at both ends of the cost/complexity range are the TF2015 which sells for around £700, and the TF2006/1 which sells for no less than £3000. If you are not prepared to mortgage your house several times over for one of these, and your interests lie between 85kHz and 25MHz, the TF144G is a good choice. But get an overhauled and guaranteed instrument, and it might be as well to get your floor boards checked!

### R.F. Oscillator Kits

As with other instrument kits, the principal supplier of kits in the UK is Heathkit, based at Gloucester. They offer their RF-1U and A/IG-102 kits, and both are excellent examples of this type of instrument. They also provide the cheapest f.m. stereo generator, this being the model IG-37.

### Home Made Oscillators

It is not beyond the capabilities of anyone so interested and experienced to build an r.f. oscillator, and indeed some enthusiasts go so far as to wind their own coils, an undertaking requiring more than ordinary interest and care. Several designs have been published in the electronic periodicals, including one that I built for a friend several years ago, and that was published in the *Radio Constructor* in 1966. This used valves, and was still in use until very recently. The chief problem of home constructed oscillators is that of accurate frequency calibration; given careful and methodical workmanship it should be possible to construct an oscillator equal to, and possibly better than, some of the cheaper commercial instruments.

## Using R.F. Oscillators and Sig-Gens

Since both are sources of radio frequencies and voltages, periodical checks on calibration accuracy are highly desirable, and more particularly where a high degree of accuracy is expected. Frequency calibration is undoubtedly easier to measure to a very high degree of accuracy, since standard frequency radio transmissions are available for the cost of a simple receiver. Alternatively, a frequency counter can be used or, failing that, a built-in, or external crystal calibrator.

Voltage checks are more difficult, and one possibility is the thermocouple meter. This being a low resistance device requiring appreciable power, will load the output, and so introduce its own errors, and it is therefore very tempting to either rely on the built-in thermocouple meter—if fitted—or not to bother at all.

Fig. 4.13   Avo model HF134 r.f. signal generator.

An alternative possibility is the use of semiconductor rectifiers preceding the moving coil meter, but this implies the use of a sensitive meter movement, and may be limited by the conduction voltage of the diodes used, since the input to the rectifiers must be great enough to overcome the non-conducting portion of the diode's characteristics. Such a device, on its own, is an inherently low impedance one, again requiring appreciable power, unless there is sufficient voltage available to enable a customary series voltage multiplying resistor to be fitted. Nevertheless, for the oscillator lacking such a device, it may prove to be a useful addition, and as such is worthy of some experimentation.

**Leakage Voltages**

A check on unwanted, leakage, voltages is very necessary where very low level work is involved on sensitive receivers, and can, very fortunately, be easily effected. All that is required is a very sensitive receiver which is then fed with a signal at the microvolt level. The sig-gen attenuator—for service oscillators are of no use here—is then gradually reduced to zero, when the receiver output should also reduce to zero. All is then well. But if the receiver output does not reduce to zero, then the sig-gen has a dangerously high leakage level, and must not be relied upon for such work. The cure is obvious!

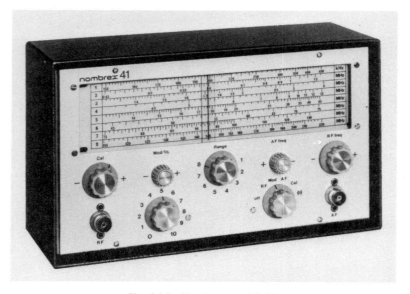

Fig. 4.14   Nombrex model 41.

Even with transistored instruments, an adequate warming up time must be allowed; with valve instruments at least $\frac{1}{2}$ hour is essential. The instrument's instruction book should clearly state if a warming up period is required, and if so the duration. Even if a warming up period is not called for, it is no bad idea to allow one, even if for no other reason than an extended period for collecting one's wits a little closer to one.

## Terminating the Output

Great care must be taken when terminating the output from r.f. oscillators, more particularly sig-gens. In the latter, the internal set-level meter will not prove to be as useful and accurate as intended, and the output from the attenuators may be quite different from the indicated value, and the reason is again one of p.d. and e.m.f. and load resistances. The use of cables of the correct impedance is also important, otherwise errors due to mismatch will occur, particularly at high frequencies. In both instances it is assumed that work to a high degree of accuracy is required.

For non-critical work, it is sometimes permissible to save time by omitting some of the procedures required for high accuracy work. It is worth remembering, however, that skipping procedures is an accumulative habit, and a bad one really, and one that will inevitably catch you out sooner than later. It is a question of balance, and of knowing when to do it and when not to. If in doubt, don't!

Some sig-gens with a built in thermocouple meter for level setting, do not take kindly to the output being short circuited, or fed into a low resistance at maximum output as the thermocouple is overloaded and promptly gives up the ghost, requiring replacement, a procedure which, unless carried out carefully, will result in inaccuracies.

## Input Impedance

The input impedance of a receiver is not resistive, obviously, but varies with the frequency in use, and the voltage set up across the input is dependent on the series impedance of the sig-gen, as already discussed. To enable some degree of standardisation to be established on m.f. receivers a standard 'dummy' aerial is inserted in series with the sig-gen output.

Fig. 4.15 shows a circuit that can easily be constructed and built into, for example, a tobacco tin. The value of R1 is dependent upon the source resistance of the sig-gen, and must be selected such that $R1 = 80 - Rs$, where Rs is the source resistance of the sig-gen. Since the source resistance of some sig-gens varies, unfortunately, according to the output voltage, increasing with increasing voltage,

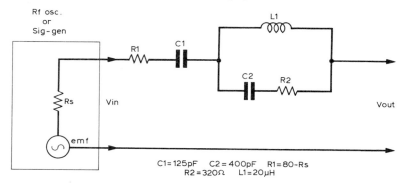

Fig. 4.15   Standard dummy aerial.

the dummy aerial may not fulfill *all* requirements. Nevertheless, it is a useful device; under known conditions its use is indespensible.

## Output Connectors

R.F. oscillators and sig-gens use a variety of output connectors, and not all manufacturers use the same types, and this is one good reason for purchasing all your instruments, where possible of course, from one manufacturer for he should standardise on one particular connector for all his instruments. Another is that should you lose a connector you will rapidly discover just how expensive replacements can be; often, due to specialised components/construction D.I.Y. self-help is not possible, and so unused leads and connectors should be carefully stored where they cannot be lost or damaged.

The r.f. output from the oscillator, or sig-gen, must always be kept to a minimum, as this avoids overloading the receiver with consequent spurious instability, overloading, and their attendant problems. Also, unless a.g.c. characteristics are of interest, it is usual to disable the a.g.c. line. With wobbulators, particularly, overloading must be avoided as incorrect traces will be obtained, leading to incorrect conclusions being drawn.

## Marker Facilities

The provision of marker 'pips', which can either be aurally detected or which can be seen on an oscilloscope trace, is an invaluable adjunct to any r.f. oscillator. The marker generator may be fixed in frequency, in which case its position on the trace will depend upon its frequency relative to the main oscillator frequency, or if it is variable, its position can be used to very accurately define the limits of the bandwidth of interest, the ultimate accuracy being dependent on the marker oscillator accuracy.

If we consider Fig. 4.16 we can see that the response curve occupies a total of 300kHz, and if the i.f. is 10·7MHz the skirt will extend from 10·55MHz to 10·85MHz. A single marker pip, depending upon its frequency, may appear anywhere along the response curve, provided of course that it is within the limits defined above.

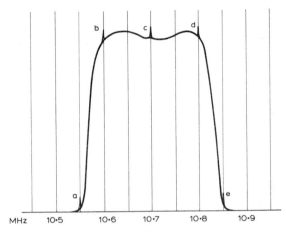

Fig. 4.16   Response curve of 10·7MHz i.f. showing fixed frequency marker pip at central frequency (c). Variable frequency pips marker can be traversed from (a) through (b), (c) and (d) to (e).

If the oscilloscope has a graticule, it should be possible to arrange matters so that every centimetre division equals 100kHz, and the marker pip will therefore provide an accurate indication of bandwidth, providing that the response curve is symmetrical. Lack of symmetry is no obstacle to the variable frequency marker since its position on the response curve can be directly related to its own calibrated frequency scales.

## Use of Marker Oscillator

The amplitude of the marker oscillator must be kept to the minimum, consistent with a discernible pip on the oscilloscope screen. Excessive amplitude of the marker oscillator will affect the r.f. oscillator (wobbulator) and will provide a distorted response curve, causing the uninitiated to seek non-existant faults.

# CHAPTER FIVE

# ATTENUATORS

MANY EQUIPMENTS PRODUCE, and many other equipments cannot
accept, signals of a magnitude that is thereby somewhat of an
embarrassment, and an intermediary device is required to reduce
the signal to a level that will prove acceptable to the receiving
equipment. Such devices are known collectively as attenuators.

It can be as simple as two resistors in series, as shown in Fig. 5.1.
Here, the attenuation afforded is dependent on the ratios of R1 to
R2, and is given very simply as $R2 = R_T/n$ where $R_T$ is the com-
bined resistance of $R1 + R2$, and n is the required attenuation ratio.
R1 is then given by $R_T - R2$. Suppose we want to reduce a voltage
by a factor of 10, and $R_T$ has to be—the reason is here irrelevant—
$1000\Omega$. We then have $1000/10 = 100$, and this is the value of R2.

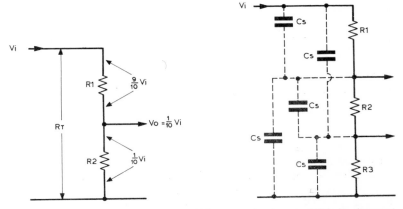

Fig. 5.1 (left) 10:1 L attenuator. Whatever the input, 9/10 is dropped
across R1, leaving the required 1/10 across R2, providing the output is not
loaded.

Fig. 5.2 (right) L attenuator, showing stray capacitances.

R1 is then $1000 - 100\Omega$ or $900\Omega$; 9/10ths of the signal is dropped across R1, leaving 1/10th across R2.

## Requirements

From such a simple, fixed, attenuator, it is but a simple step to an extension which allows a number of steps to be provided for, and this is shown in Fig. 5.3. Let us now make $R_T = 1M\Omega$, and $n = 1/10$, 1/100 and 1/1000. Straight away we can say that $R4 = 10^6/10^3$ or $1000\Omega$. R3 is then equal to $10^6/10^2$ or $10k\Omega$. But, we must not forget R4, and so R3 is actually $10k\Omega - 1k\Omega$, or $9k\Omega$. R2 is then $10^6/10$ or $100k\Omega$. But we have already calculated R3 as $10k\Omega$ (actually R3 + R4) so that R2 is actually $100k\Omega - 10k\Omega$ or $90k\Omega$. Lastly, R1 is $= R_T - R2 + R3 + R4$, or $10^6 - 100k\Omega$, or $900k\Omega$.

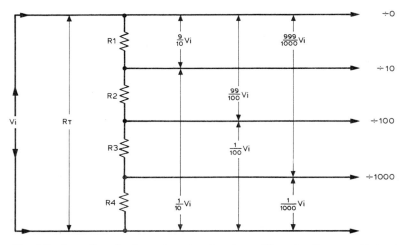

Fig. 5.3   4-position L attenuator, showing how different ratios are obtained for any input voltage.

As a final cross check, add all the individual resistances together; they should total $R_T$; if they don't then something is wrong! The number of steps is immaterial, so long as the last, or bottom, resistance is calculated first, then *up* the line, arriving at R1 = R2 = R3 + + + + Rx. The last crosscheck is essential to ensure that all the calculations have been correctly performed.

Such an attenuator is adequate for d.c. and for low frequencies, and depending on the total resistance ($R_T$) and on the layout of the attenuator, and hence on its losses, the lowest frequency capable of

being handled without excessive losses may be only a few hundreds
of Hz. This is due to the capacitance that exists between components,
and between them and earth, shown simplified in Fig. 5.2 where Cs
represents the stray capacitances. Losses can be counteracted, to
some extent, by deliberately placing capacitors across each resistance
such that the capacitors increase in value in proportion to the
resistive attenuation factors, as shown, arbitrarily, in Fig. 5.4.
The trick is to 'swamp' the unknown capacitances out and to replace
them with predictable, lump, capacitances.

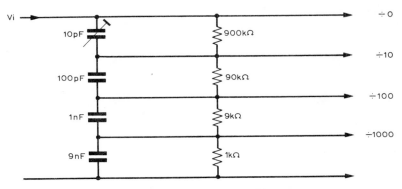

Fig. 5.4   Frequency compensation of L attenuator.

With skill and care, it is possible to produce an aperiodic attenuator, at least up to several hundred kHz. The attenuation of such
an attenuator is dependent very greatly upon the load into which it
works, and is only the calculated value when the load is infinite,
i.e. the grid of a valve or the gate of an IGFET. Anything less, and
errors will occur; the lower the load impedance, the greater the
error. Also, the input impedance may be affected, and this may not
always be acceptable to the preceding device.

The ideal attenuator would have constant input and output
impedances, so that the preceding, and following, circuitry is not
affected. While the ideal is not a practicable proposition, it is
possible to approach very closely to it, and for most practical
purposes it is completely acceptable to use different attenuator
configurations. These are of two basic types, with their derivatives.
The two basic types are the T and the $\pi$, as shown in Fig. 5.5a, b;
their derivatives being shown in Fig. 5.5c, d, e.

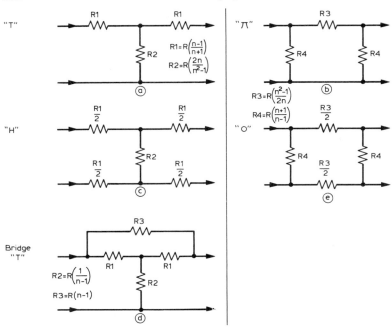

Fig. 5.5    T and $\pi$ attenuator sections.

## Individual Attenuators

It is convenient to look upon attenuators in their individual configurations, as we looked at the potential divider of Fig. 5.1. The
formulae are very simple, though a little tedious where numerous
attenuation factors have to be worked out. Looking at the basic T,
we see that it comprises three resistances, two being equal. R = the
input/output impedance required, while n = the attenuation ratio
required. R1 is then given by

$$R\left(\frac{n-1}{n+1}\right) \text{ and R2 by } R\left(\frac{2n}{n^2-1}\right)$$

A derivative of the basic T is the H shown in Fig. 5.5c. This is
made up of two Ts placed long-leg to long-leg, giving the configuration so aptly named. The calculations are as for the basic T,
with the exception that the series resistances have to be halved, the
parallel resistance remaining unchanged. The major derivative of
the T is the bridge T, shown in Fig. 5.5d, and to illustrate its import-

ance it has its own design formulae. R1 is equal to the required input/output impedance, and so is duplicated, the attenuation ratios then being dependent on the values assigned to R2 and R3. R2 = $R(1/n - 1)$ and R3 = $R(n - 1)$.

The basic $\pi$ consists of three resistances, two again being equal, and the formulae are

$$R3 = R\left(\frac{n^2 - 1}{2n}\right) \text{ and } R4 = R\left(\frac{n + 1}{n - 1}\right).$$

The derivative of the $\pi$ is the parallel $\pi$ (0) and this consists of two $\pi$s placed long-legs to long-legs, giving the configuration showed in Fig. 5.5e. The calculations are as for the basic $\pi$ with the series resistances halved, the parallel resistances remaining unchanged.

So far, we have only mentioned that R must equal the required input/output impedance, and now one of the characteristics of these attenuators must be further discussed. Unlike the L attenuators of Fig. 5.1 and Fig. 5.2 which require that the load be infinite, these attenuators require that both the input and the output resistances are precisely defined, otherwise the attenuation actually obtained will not be the calculated value.

**Recurrent Attenuators**

It is possible to connect any number of individual attenuators in series to provide any number of attenuation steps, a very common requirement. These steps need not necessarily be equal, but most commonly are, and will be so treated. If we consider a number of $\pi$ steps in series, we arrive at the configuration shown in Fig. 5.6. The individual sections can be calculated as shown in Fig. 5.5b.

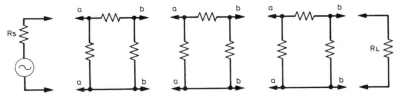

Fig. 5.6 $\pi$ attenuators in series. Each individual stage forms the load for the adjacent stage.

Looking at the end section of Fig. 5.6, the resistance across terminals a-a, when the load, R$_L$, is connected is equal to R$_L$, and the same state of affairs applies whichever sections are joined together, since each forms the load for the other. When they are all joined together as in Fig. 5.7, opposing resistances can be replaced by one having half the value of the individual resistances, and this applies irrespective of the number of sections, always assuming that equal attenuation ratios are involved.

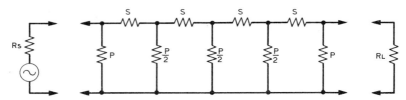

Fig. 5.7   Individual stages joined together. When individual stages are joined together the parallel resistors can be as shown.

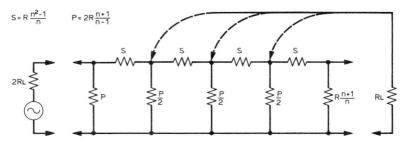

Fig. 5.8   Connection of load into centre section of multiway attenuator. The load, when connected in the centre sections, has elements on both sides, requiring the resistors to be calculated as shown.

However, the load when connected into circuit finds *two* resistances, one to either side when in the middle, and this will upset our careful calculations; but, by a little bit of juggling it is possible to meet the stated requirements, as shown in Fig. 5.8. This requires a little clarification. The load matches the attenuator between the points to which it is connected, i.e. anywhere along the chain; the source and effective part of the attenuator are, however, mismatched by working into the tail of the attenuator in parallel with the load. The total power received is therefore less than it would be with perfect matching, and works out at $-3$dB. Fortunately, this power loss is constant at all points along the chain and the attenuation factors are therefore unchanged, as is the resistance seen by the load.

## Attenuator Switching

The basic T, the bridge T, and the $\pi$ are unbalanced configurations, to be connected into a circuit where the earth, or chassis, is a common terminal. The H and the O are balanced configurations, to be connected into circuits where the signal is balanced with respect to earth, or chassis, with either side being live. Switching of unbalanced attenuators can be accomplished in several ways; a single-pole multiway rotary switch can be used, as shown in Fig. 5.9, or a number of two-pole two-way switches can be used as shown in Fig. 5.10. The former has the attraction of simplicity and relative cheapness; the latter, while being more expensive in terms of switches is more amenable to construction in a form which greatly reduces mutual capacitance.

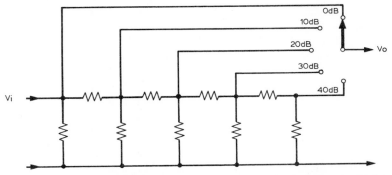

Fig. 5.9   Rotary switch used to switch select the required attenuation ratios.

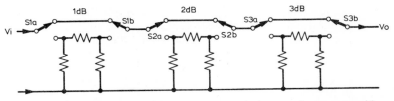

Fig. 5.10   Multiswitch attenuator. When all switches are in upper position, there is zero attenuation. With switches in lower position, attenuation is introduced, being equal to any single switch depressed or to the sum of the depressed switches.

Balanced attenuators are more expensive to produce since extra resistors are required, and the number of poles must be doubled. This can be seen if we imagine Fig. 5.9 and Fig. 5.10 as being in mirror image.

At a.f., stray capacitances and inductances can be greatly ignored, unless the attenuator is ill constructed with no thought to correct layout. The higher the frequency, the greater the difficulty in preventing the attenuator being bypassed by stray capacitances, or made more inaccurate by series inductances. The problem is more acute if high value resistors are involved, since the magnitudes of the stray capacitances can be appreciably lower than the values of the—required—resistive attenuator sections.

## Choosing an Attenuator

More properly, this should be defined as an a.f. attenuator, since all r.f. sig-gens have suitable built-in attenuators. Attenuators are generally designed to work from d.c. up to some frequency in the low r.f. If transformers are involved, as they are in the more versatile attenuators, the frequency coverage will automatically be restricted to the a.f. If the transformer can be switched out of circuit at will, there will be two ranges: a.f. and d.c. to the low r.f.

Inevitably, the first decision must be that of deciding how much can be spent, since this defines the terms of reference in respect of facilities and accuracy. For general purposes, a range of at least 60dB is desirable, a modest 1000:1 ratio. Ideally, 100 or 120dB is highly desirable, and will very greatly extend the usefulness of the attenuator, i.e. extended ratios of $10^5:1$ and $10^6:1$.

Knowing the output of an a.f. oscillator—for this is primarily what the attenuator will be used with—it is possible to make a decision of the total attenuation required, and here experience and circumstances will prove vitally important. Then purely as a contingency against future, as yet unknown, requirements, it is prudent to add on at least another 20dB. However, it must be admitted that much good work can be carried out with an attenuator having much less than the theoretical maximum desirable, and my own home-made attenuator with a range of only 31dB is quite adequate for such work as frequency response plotting, where a range of $\pm20$dB is normally the limit.

Having decided on the maximum range required, we must next decide how best to provide this, and upon the steps—of individual attenuation—required. Ideally, for speed of operation, coupled to precise resolution, several steps are required (coarse, medium, and fine) and these can be provided if we split the steps into, for example, 10 steps of 10dB each, 10 steps of 1dB each, and 10 steps of 0·1dB each, giving a total of 111dB, and such an attenuator would be a marvellous instrument to own and use. In the interests of economy, some of the steps could be curtailed or even totally omitted, and one possibility is to omit the 0·1dB steps and reduce the number of 10dB steps.

An alternative approach is the two-pole two-way switch system already referred to. In this, a number of attenuation steps are provided such that each is precisely half, or twice, the preceding one, the usual configuration being 1dB, 2dB, 4dB, 8dB, 16dB, 32dB for the individual stages, which are used either on their own, as shown, or in cascade to provide attenuation ratios not included. 3dB would therefore be 1dB + 2dB, and 7dB would be 1dB + 2dB + 4dB, and so on, and the same plan would be followed if fractional dB ratios were included. Since the errors may be cumulative—they can also cancel out!—it is necessary to provide a much higher degree of accuracy for the individual stages than if only one stage was involved, for example a single 7dB stage instead of three in cascade.

Whatever system is used, the smallest increment available should be 1dB, and this will prove suitable if basic servicing or mundane design/development is involved. For design/development, and servicing also, to precisely defined limits, a much smaller increment is essential, and 0·1dB should suffice for such applications. It is little use having such small increments if the tolerance is greater than the smallest increment, and if we stick to the proposal made in an earlier chapter about equipment accuracy, we will require the accuracy to be at least × 5 better than the smallest increment, i.e. $\pm 0·02$dB, and this is where our bank balance is liable to feel a little bit thin!

## Power Dissipation

Attenuators consist almost exclusively of resistors, and these are rated for power dissipation in terms of watts. This, of course, means that we cannot feed in any old voltage and expect it to be attenuated. It may be, for a period of time before the resistors burn out! Even if they are not actually burnt out, they may suffer permanent damage in the form of altered resistances, and accuracy will clearly suffer.

The implications of this are quite simple. Calculate the maximum voltage you are likely to require attenuating and purchase an attenuator to suit. In the event of your voltage requirements being so excessive that a commercial attenuator will not prove suitable, you have the choice of either decreasing your voltage, building your own attenuator to suit, or risking damage to the commercial attenuator you purchase.

**Balanced or Unbalanced**

Then we come to the point where we have to decide: balanced or unbalanced. Quite simply this means that the signal voltage is either above, or below, earth potential, with the earth being common, or that the signal is both above, and below, earth potential, i.e. is floating.

Unbalanced attenuators are cheaper, and have a much wider frequency response, than balanced attenuators, for the simple reason that the latter require a transformer, or transformers, with which to provide a balanced, centre tapped, input/output. Wide band transformers with a high power capability are both bulky and expensive, and as a compromise it is not uncommon to restrict the bandwidth to the a.f., i.e. 20Hz to 20kHz.

Attenuators, as we saw earlier, are designed to work into, and with, a specific impedance. For general a.f. work, this is commonly 600$\Omega$, either balanced or unbalanced or both. Those containing a transformer sometimes offer alternative output impedances, 150$\Omega$ and 75$\Omega$ being common values.

**Commercial Attenuators**

Commercial attenuators, like other measuring instruments, should be provided with a specification showing the limits of permissible error and the power that the attenuator can handle without damage; sometimes the maximum voltage input is specified, and in my own opinion this is the safest and least ambiguous way of specifying the maximum input.

Since the attenuators we have been looking at, apart from the L type, are of the loaded variety, it is highly desirable that an internal resistor, of the appropriate values, is incorporated, to be switched in when high input impedances have to be worked into; we will not always be fortunate enough to encounter equipments considerate enough to incorporate the appropriate input impedances!

Attenuators can be obtained from a number of manufacturers. Probably the most comprehensive is the Marconi TF2160 'Monitored Attenuator'. This incorporates an integral voltmeter to monitor incoming voltages, and has a specification too comprehensive to be listed here! A somewhat simpler model is their TF2162, shown in Fig. 5.11. The Advance A64A is an even simpler attenuator, offering 0-70dB attenuation, in six steps of 10dB and ten steps of 1dB. Fig. 5.12 shows the circuit.

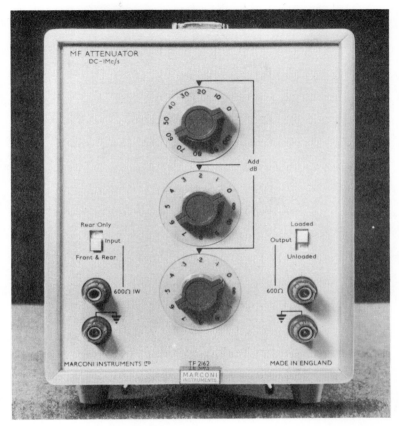

Fig. 5.11   Marconi TF2162MF attenuator, giving 111dB in steps of 10dB, 1dB and 0·1dB.

## Home Made Attenuators

As far as the a.f. and low r.f. are concerned, the individual can build an excellent attenuator for himself, using the principles outlined earlier, provided, as usual, that he is prepared to indulge in a few simple maths and in some careful and painstaking work when actually building the unit. Fig. 5.13 shows such an attenuator that I built for my own use several years ago, and which was featured in *Practical Electronics* for November 1974. This is of the multi-switch π type, a personal design favourite, and has a maximum

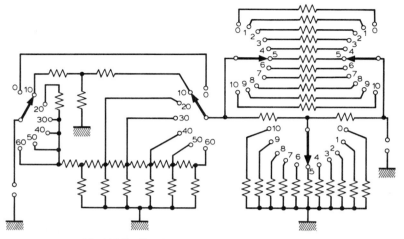

Fig. 5.12    Circuit of Advance A64A attenuator.

Fig. 5.13    Author's home-built attenuator of $5\pi$ sections giving a total of 31dB attenuation.

deviation of $-\frac{1}{2}$dB at 100kHz when the total attenuation is switched into circuit, and when terminated in a 600Ω ± 1% load.

## Using Attenuators

The principle to bear in mind is that an attenuator is used to counteract the characteristics of any equipment it is used in conjunction with, the attenuator settings being a function of the equipment's deviation—intentional or otherwise—from a previously established datum point. One of the great attractions of this type of measuring setup is that the indicating instrument, be it voltmeter or oscilloscope, need not be calibrated or even accurate! Provided it is gain-stable over the bandwidth of interest, virtually anything can be used as an indicator.

The attenuator most commonly, but not invariably, follows the a.f. oscillator, as shown in Fig. 5.14. Greater accuracy is ensured if a single indicator is used to measure the input to the attenuator and the output from the power amplifier, since only a single instrument error has to be allowed for instead of two if two separate instruments are used.

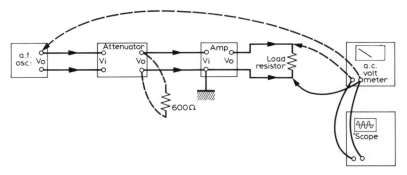

Fig. 5.14 Measuring frequency response of power amplifier. An external 600 Ω load must be used if the attenuator does not incorporate an internal 600 Ω load resistor. The amplifier load resistor must be suitable for the output impedance and power rating of the amplifier.

The use of switches to switch the indicator from input to output looks attractive on circuit diagrams and is undoubtedly easier to use in practice. Also in practice, switches have self capacitance, and the wiring, inevitably, is compelled to run in close proximity, increasing that self capacitance so that the end result is virtually certain to be instability where high gain amplifiers are concerned. Flying leads, though less convenient, are amenable to being routed to avoid areas of high gain, and so are shown in Fig. 5.14, and are highly recommended.

### Frequency Response Checks

In use, plotting a frequency response curve of an amplifier, for instance, the attenuator has a small amount of attenuation inserted prior to commencing the test; if the deviation is expected to lie within ±3dB, a total of, say 6dB can be inserted to allow for unexpected deviations, and always supposing the conditions of the test, i.e. the voltage input available, and the output voltage/power required, permit of such an attenuation being used.

A datum point must be established on the indicator at the commonly used mid-band frequency of 1kHz. The a.f. oscillator is then reduced in frequency at octave steps, closer if required, and any deviation required on the attenuator to restore the *original* datum point is noted. The 1kHz datum is rechecked, and then the oscillator is increased in frequency, again at the required intervals, the attenuator being used if necessary to restore the original datum point. The overall frequency bandwidth will be dependent upon individual circumstances, i.e. the applied criteria and the equipment available.

## Tone Control Circuits

Tone control circuits can be checked along similar lines. Supposing bass or treble boost must be checked, the datum is again established at 1kHz, with zero attenuation inserted via the attenuator. The frequency is then increased at the required intervals, and as the output increases due to the treble boost, so the attenuator is correspondingly brought into circuit to restore the original datum point. Bass boost, of course, requires that the frequency is reduced, the attenuator settings being noted as before.

Bass or treble cut is checked similarly, this time with a predetermined amount of attenuation inserted prior to the test. Most tone controls offer a maximum cut or boost of around 15dB, though a few exceed these limits. Therefore we can expect to insert at least 15dB into circuit when establishing a datum at 1kHz, and as the cut begins to make its effect felt, so attenuation is removed to restore the original datum point. Bass cut is measured with a falling frequency, treble cut with an increasing frequency.

One factor should emerge as experience with an attenuator is gained. This is a very speedy way of checking frequency response, since one does not have to peer at what may be a very badly cramped meter scale, only at a previously established datum point.

Having established a set of attenuator readings, corresponding to the frequency response of a circuit, it is often necessary to draw this up on graph paper. This is now of the metric variety, having a vertical, or Y axis, in centimetres, the horizontal, or X axis, being logarithmic. For an extended frequency response, what is commonly referred to as 4 cycle log-by-centimetre paper can be used, and this will accomodate a range of 10Hz to 100kHz. For a more restricted range in greater detail, 3 cycle or 2 cycle paper can be used. Curiously, this sort of graph paper is a commodity that I have always found to be somewhat elusive, enquiries being met with blank looks unless a more knowledgeable assistant is around, and I now go armed with a sample when embarking on a 'graph paper mission'.

# CHAPTER SIX

# OSCILLOSCOPES

THERE WAS A TIME when practicing engineers were firmly entrenched in one of two bitterly opposed camps: the antagonists, to whom the 'scope was a prime time wasting instrument, and the protagonists, to whom it was the ultimate instrument. The former have been routed—well, nearly!—and there is now almost general agreement on the oscilloscope's great usefulness. Indeed, many engineers, if restricted solely to one instrument, would unhesitatingly choose a 'scope.

Why? Well, a good modern instrument, in fine condition, will enable a trained operator to make measurements to an accuracy of better than 5%, approaching closely the limits of permissible error of many analogoue instruments. Since it draws instant graphs of voltages, or currents, that vary with time, it enables measurements to be made of irregular, or one-shot, waveforms, of both period and magnitude, something no other instrument can match.

Prior to the development of the electro-mechanical pen-and-paper-strip chart recorder, which itself has severe limitations in respect of frequency response, the only way of measuring voltages or currents that varied with time was to laboriously make readings of the magnitude of the voltage or current being investigated, relate these to time elapsed, and then draw a graph by hand. Apart from the tedium, the voltage or current had to be considerate enough to vary slowly enough for the unfortunate operator to note both magnitude and time!

Two basic phenomena are responsible for the success of the 'scope. The first is an electron beam, virtually without mass, and hence inertia, which upon striking a suitable screen makes that screen fluoresce (i.e. emit light in the visible part of the spectrum) almost irrespective of the rate of change of the beam. The second is the persistence of vision of the human eye. Let us look at these mysteries a little closer.

Persistence of vision is a phenomenon with which most people are familiar, if only unknowingly. Most of us, in our younger and care-free years, will have flashed a hand-torch at a wall during darkness to produce patterns. Science tells us that the spot of light is just a spot of light, but our eyes tell us that it is a continuous line. Any bright light produces an effect upon the retina of the eye, an effect which lingers for a time after the cause has been removed, whether totally, i.e. a light switched off, or a light that has been moved from one place to another, hence the continuous line if the beam from the torch is moved fast enough.

## Focusing the Beam

The fluorescing of a screen is effected by an electron beam impinging upon a screen coated with a fluorescent material. This is the cathode ray tube, or c.r.t., the heart of the oscilloscope. The screen of such a c.r.t., without focusing electrodes would present a patch of light of indeterminate size and shape because, on their way to the screen, the electrons would be subject to dispersion. Some way of focusing such a beam is therefore required.

Focusing is effected by a series of anodes placed after the cathode which cause the electron stream to converge and produce a small spot upon the screen. The electron-producing cathode is virtually surrounded by the grid, which is, of course, negative with respect to the cathode, and therefore repels the electrons emitted by the cathode. Cunningly, a small exit hole is provided at the forward end of the grid, and the electrons steam out of this and immediately start to diverge.

This is not what is required, so a (first) anode is designed to limit the spread of the electron beam, which then encounters the field of a second anode. This acts as a converging 'lens' to reproduce a more-or-less sharply defined spot upon the screen. Variations in brilliance are effected by altering the voltage of the grid relative to the cathode; the intensity of the spot is decreased as the grid is made more negative, and increased as it is made more positive. Focusing is effected by altering the potential of the first anode which is also relative to the cathode.

## Deflecting the Beam

Deflection of the electron beam can be by means of an electrostatic field or a magnetic field. Magnetic deflection, commonly used for TV purposes, cannot cope with the requirements of normal oscilloscopic work since the coils limit the rate of change of magnetic flux producing current unless sinusoidal, low frequency, work is involved. Electrostatic deflection is therefore universally used for oscilloscopic purposes.

The electron beam is, for practical purposes, without inertia or weight, and is therefore easy to deflect up to frequencies so high that visualising the effect is extremely difficult. Deflection of the beam is achieved by two additional sets of electrodes, Y1-Y2 and X1-X2. In mathematical notation, the vertical axis is labelled the Y axis, and the horizontal axis the X axis, and thus the Y electrodes, (more commonly called 'plates') deflect the beam vertically, above and below the centre line, while the X plates deflect the beam horizontally, to the left and right of centre.

Electrons, being negatively charged, are attracted to the plate carrying a positive charge, and are repelled by a negatively charged plate. By varying the charge on the plates, relative to each other, it is possible to position the beam anywhere on the screen, or off it. If all plates carry an equal charge, and assuming that the c.r.t. is perfectly symmetrical in its sensitivity, the beam will impinge in the centre of the screen.

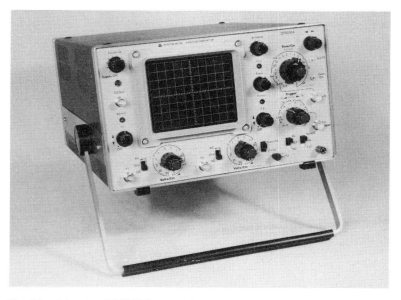

Fig. 6.1 Advance OS1000A general purpose oscilloscope covering d.c. to 20MHz.

By making Y1 more positive than Y2, or, since it amounts to the same thing, making Y2 more negative than Y1, we can make the beam occupy a position above the centre line of the screen. Similarly with X1 and X2 plates in the horizontal plane. If the spot is made to traverse to and fro in any direction, due to the persistence of vision, aided a little by the persistence of the tube, a continuous line will be formed.

Electrostatic c.r.t.'s are available in different sizes with different characteristics, so it is possible to select a tube to suit virtually all requirements. Sizes range from 1″ up to 6″ for general applications. A fascinating little oscilloscope of the early 50's was the GEC *Miniscope* using a $1\frac{1}{2}$″ tube, and within its intended applications was a useful little instrument. Of the 6″ tubes, possibly the most famous for amateur applications was the ex-radar VCR97; my own home made oscilloscope uses one of these.

### Sensitivity

Like thermionic valves, c.r.t.'s are rated in terms of grid voltage, cathode voltage, and assorted anode voltages. The voltage between cathode and grid determines the brilliance of the spot, and is usually quoted in terms of the voltage required for cut-off, i.e. for the spot to be extinguished.

The sensitivity of the deflection plates is usually expressed as a shift in the spot for a given applied voltage, i.e. x mm/V. This is dependent in turn upon the voltage applied to the final, or 3rd anode, so that a formula is frequently quoted in the form $S = k/Va3$ where k is a constant and $Va3$ is the final anode potential.

Since the Y plates are nearer to the grid, the voltage required to deflect the beam is less than that required for the X plates, and so two constants are quoted. Clearly, for a given value of k a high value for $Va3$ will result in a decrease in sensitivity, and vice versa.

### Phosphors

The phosphor with which the internal face of the c.r.t. is coated is dependent upon the application. For general purpose use, a green medium-persistence phosphor is used, with a blue/green medium-persistence phosphor as an alternative. For the study of very short duration phenomena, a long-persistence phosphor must be used since it keeps the image on the screen for several seconds after the phenomena has ceased. For very high speed phenomena, a short-persistence phosphor must be used to stop the image blurring and smearing. For photographic purposes, a short-persistence blue phosphor is commonly used.

The persistence of the phosphor is denoted in one of several ways, of which the American notation is the most used. Here, P1 denotes a green/medium-persistence phosphor, P2 blue/green medium, P5 blue/very short. Long-persistence tubes operate with a combination of fluorescence and phosphorescence.

If we imagine a pulse modulating the electron beam, we can see that it takes a certain amount of time—dependent on the phosphor used—for the fluorescence to build up to maximum; the pulse then ceases and a period of decay begins during which the phosphor lives up to its name and phosphoresces, gradually diminishing in intensity until it ceases to emit light. We therefore have two states; t1 and t2, or build-up and decay.

The brilliance of the display on the c.r.t. is of great importance when viewing waveforms having—relatively—low repetition frequencies with very rapidly changing portions, i.e. squarewaves and the like. The verticals of such waveforms can change from one state to another in $\mu$S or nS, and are usually invisible on even good quality oscilloscopes. The writing speed—the term is self explanatory—is dependent upon the final, or A3, potential, and this, as we have seen, also controls the sensitivity of the tube. More sensitive X and Y amplifiers are therefore required to compensate.

## Post Deflection Anodes

A way round this problem of sensitivity is to deflect the electron beam while it is travelling along at a comparatively leisurely rate, and then to accelerate it. This permits the conflicting requirements of high brilliance and high sensitivity to be adequately met. The method is known as post deflection acceleration, or p.d.a.

Originally, this was achieved by coating the inside of the tube with graphite, in two sections insulated from each other, The section nearer the electron gun was connected to the final anode, or to a potential of the same magnitude, with a further accelerating potential applied between the two sections. Since we seldom get anything without paying a penalty, the result was distortion if the deflection potentials were at all wide, as it had to be to obtain maximum brilliance.

Reduction of the distortion was effected by coating the inside of the tube with a resistive material, in the form of a spiral, and extending from near the deflector plates to near the screen, and terminated at both ends. The end nearer the plates is connected to the final anode, that at the screen end being connected to the aluminised screen and to the accelerating potential. Adequate brilliance can be provided by such means, even for wideband use, with minimal distortion, provided that an adequately high p.d.a. voltage is used; p.d.a. voltages range from around 3–4kV to 20kV in high speed oscilloscopes.

### Double Beam Tubes

It is frequently required to display two—or more—quantities simultaneously on one screen; these can be a pair of voltages, or a voltage and a current converted to a voltage by being dropped across a suitable resistor. C.R.T.'s are available with more than one electron gun and multiple deflecting systems, but the most common is one electron gun with a beam splitting plate, providing two vertical or Y channels, with a common X channel enabling real time measurements to be made, since phase relationships—assuming amplifier equality—are identical.

The splitting of the beam is effected by a very thin plate in close proximity to the final anode of the complete gun. Since this plate is in the path of the electron beam, this splits into two streams, each affected—in theory at least—by its own deflector plate, since the splitter plate provides screening between the two sets of Y deflector plates. The screening is not total, and some crosstalk between channels is inevitable, but can be further minimised by additional electrodes. A disadvantage is that the brilliance is reduced by half.

### HORIZONTAL DEFLECTION

We have seen how, when an appropriate voltage is applied to the deflection plates, the spot can be positioned anywhere on or off the screen, and how if the rate of change is rapid enough a continuous line will be formed.

On a graph containing time versus another quantity, it is customary to represent time on the horizontal (or X) axis, with the other quantity represented on the vertical (or Y) axis. In our case, the other quantity will be a voltage or a current converted into a voltage. On an oscilloscope, therefore, we require a voltage varying with time to be applied to the X plates, but it must be a rather special kind of voltage. The X voltage must increase in proportion to the time elapsed, until it reaches a predetermined magnitude, and then must collapse very rapidly to zero. It must then do all this again at repetition frequencies ranging from several seconds per sweep to around $1\mu S$ or $0.5\mu S$ per sweep in general purpose oscilloscopes.

## The Timebase

The generation of such voltages is performed by a variety of circuits known collectively as timebases, and the ideal voltage is the sawtooth shown in Fig. 6.2a from which the derivation of the name will be obvious. The required characteristics are a perfectly linear forward sweep and a very rapid flyback, after which the forward sweep recommences, followed by the flyback, ad infinitum.

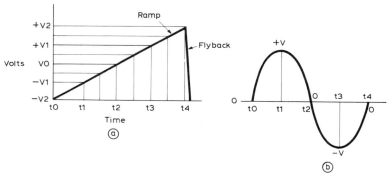

Fig. 6.2   Showing how, with voltage increasing with time, a linear ramp traces out a sinewave.

The forward sweep is normally in one direction only, left to right, but the return of the spot to its starting point must be performed as rapidly as possible otherwise the waveform will be retraced—in reverse—as well, and the confusion can well be imagined. Even so, in some cases, suppression of the flyback or retrace is essential to prevent dual traces. In order to explain the function played by the forward sweep, it is necessary to apportion voltages and times to Fig. 6.2a.

At the instant of the ramp—another, and a more appropriate, way of describing the timebase voltage—commencing, t0, the ramp voltage is $-V2$. As the ramp progresses, we reach point t1, at which point the voltage is $-V1$. The ramp still progresses, and reaches t2, at which point the voltage is 0. On it sweeps, giving us successively t3 and $+V1$, and then t4 and $+V2$, at which point it collapses rapidly back to points t0 and −V2, only to start the progression all over again. Relating the progress of the ramp in terms of Fig. 6.2b, we can see that at t0 the sinewave has yet to start, at t1 it has reached its positive peak, at t2 it has reached zero again, at t3 it is at negative peak, and at t4 is back to zero. From start to finish, the ramp therefore displays one complete cycle of the sinewave.

This is a fundamental point in oscilloscope timebases: when ramp and signal frequencies are equal, a single cycle is displayed. If the ramp frequency is lower than the signal frequency, several cycles will be displayed, in the ratio of the two frequencies. When the ramp frequency is higher than the signal frequency, less than a single cycle is displayed. The display remains stationary only when the two frequencies are equal or in integral multiple relationships; at all other frequencies the display will break up and drift.

**Linear Ramp**

The necessity for a perfectly linear ramp voltage has been referred to, and the reason for this is evident if we look at Fig. 6.3. This

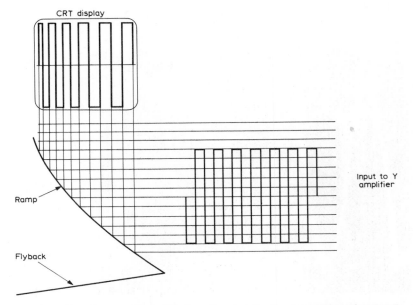

Fig. 6.3    Showing waveform non-linearity when the timebase voltage increases in a non-linear manner.

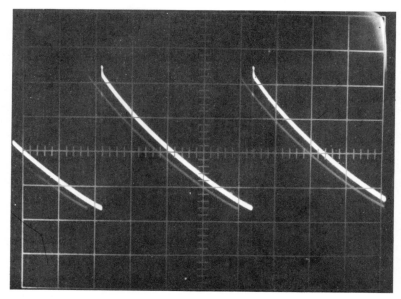

Fig. 6.4 Timebase waveform showing non-linearity and jitter and instantaneous flyback. Vertical, 20V/cm; horizontal, 1mS/cm.

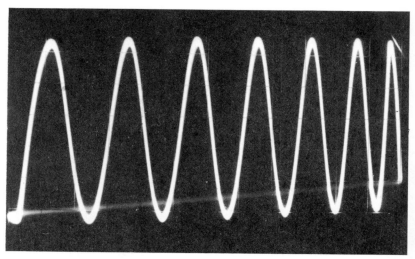

Fig. 6.5 Non-linearity produced by the trace of Fig. 6.4. The trace also shows some defocusing and the flyback has not been completely suppressed.

shows an input squarewave, used because it reveals non-linearity, and linearity, much better than a sinewave. The timebase ramp is used as a transfer device, and the non-linearity of the display is immediately obvious.

The non-linear display does not look as 'nice' as a linear ramp, but there is more to the story than just appearance. The oscilloscope is a measuring instrument, and for the accurate measurement of time a linear ramp is absolutely essential, otherwise the determination of time intervals between successive events is impracticable; not all the waveforms we want to study, and measure, are as considerate as the squarewave with its regular mark-space ratios; some are most irregular!

As an example, Fig. 6.4 shows the waveform from an old valve timebase 'scope. This is distinctly non-linear, and the faint image to the left is indicative of jitter. The display produced by this ramp is shown in Fig. 6.5, and the non-linearity is very evident. The flyback has not been fully suppressed. Such a display may be acceptable for non-critical waveform analysis but is unsuitable for time measurement for the intervals of time between successive cycles is different, and, for really critical work, the time interval between one complete cycle is not equal.

Reverting back to Fig. 6.3, the non-linearity is evidenced by compression at the left hand side of the screen; however, depending on the number of phase shifting stages the ramp passes, the cramping could well be on the other side.

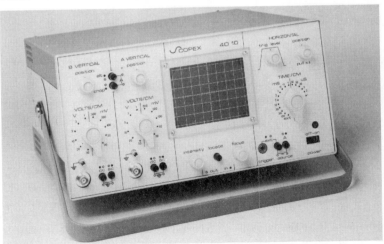

Fig. 6.6   Scopex 4D10 dual trace 10MHz oscilloscope.

## Generating the Ramp

From earliest times, from the most primitive 'scope to the most sophisticated, one factor remains in common when ramps have to be generated: the time taken by a capacitor to charge up to a given voltage via a given resistor, and Fig. 6.7a shows the essentials. The voltage rise across C1 is V2 and is exponential, taking the shape shown in Fig. 6.7b. The rate of change of V2 is proportional to its instantaneous value, and, of course, the rate of current change is the exact opposite.

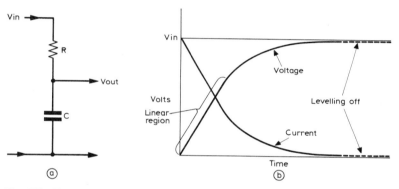

Fig. 6.7   The exponential charging voltage curve when a capacitor is charged from voltage Vin via resistance R. The charging current curve is the inverse of the charging voltage curve.

Theoretically, the capacitor never reaches V1, and therefore it might be supposed that we cannot utilise this characteristic. Fortunately, in practice, a capacitor is considered to be fully charged when the time constant, i.e. C × R, is multiplied by an arbitrary constant, in this case 5. The time constant is not the same thing, since only some 60% of the timing constant is involved, and in practice the capacitor voltage will increase fairly linearly up to this point, after which it will bend steeply.

This means that the full charging voltage cannot be used, otherwise we will end up with an exceedingly non-linear timebase. The trick is to let the capacitor charge up in the normal manner, and then while the ramp is still linear, cut it off. This provides us with a linear timebase, but the penalty to be paid is a restricted output voltage. Alternatively, the capacitor must be 'kidded' into thinking that it has a high voltage to climb up to, a commonly adopted artifice, and the way this is done is to keep the current through C and R as constant as possible.

In modern oscilloscopes, constant velocity timebase generators are used in which ramp velocity and duration are completely independent of the repetition frequency. There are very good reasons for the adoption of this philosophy. We saw, while looking at tube phosphors, that a high speed writing capability was essential if parts of the displayed waveform were not to be lost. A somewhat similar situation exists if certain types of waveform have to be examined on a simple repetitive timebase, and here it is quite possible to lose the portion of the waveform we are interested in because of the time base characteristics.

**Recurrent Timebase Generators**

A difficult waveform to examine is one consisting of short duration pulses with—comparatively—long time intervals between them. If the pulse width is of the order of $\mu$S long, with a time interval of several mS between them, it is possible to synchronise a recurrent timebase to them, but, since the timebase has to run at the repetition frequency to display a single pulse—as we saw earlier—all we are likely to see is a very thin (and dim!) line perpendicular to the timebase axis, where the trace will be exceedingly bright, since we have had to turn the brilliance up to maximum just to see our thin, dim trace.

If pairs of pulses are involved, the timebase will have to be run at a sub-multiple of the repetition frequency, and if the timebase is run at the pulse repetition frequency, one of the pulses will completely disappear, since it will have occurred during the flyback stroke! Whatever the timebase speed, we are in trouble. We either lose a pulse, if timebase and pulse repetition frequencies are identical, or they are so compressed together at the commencement of the sweep that any attempts at measurements are impossible.

A partial, but not wholly successful, solution is to increase the speed of the sweep repetition frequency of the recurrent type of timebase to the point where the sweep speed is well above that of the pulse repetition frequency, so that the outline of the pulse, or pulses, is traced out at every $n^{th}$ sweep. If this is done, some separation of the pulses *may* be possible, but of course the traces will be correspondingly dimmer. At this point one is sometimes tempted to take up innocuous sports like parachuting with the aid of a pocket handkerchief!

**Triggered Timebase Generators**

The successful measurement of such pulses—which it must be admitted are somewhat extreme for general purpose work, but which serve admirably to illustrate the problems of timebases—can be effected by using a timebase that only works when triggered by an input signal to the vertical amplifier.

In such timebases, the forward sweep velocity is independent of the repetition frequency. A single ramp is produced in response to the trigger signal, and ideally this must precede the part of the waveform to be viewed by a given time interval. For obvious reasons, this type of timebase is sometimes referred to as a stroboscopic timebase.

**Signal Delay**

In order to be successful, a special trigger pulse generator/shaper must be incorporated; a circuit which accepts any shape and amplitude of waveform and converts it into a suitable pulse for triggering the timebase. Since instantaneous starting is not possible, leading to some loss of the waveform's leading edge (the waveform to be examined, that is) it is therefore essential to include some form of longer delay after the timebase trigger output point from the Y amplifier. If this is done successfully, all portions of even very rapid waveforms can be completely examined. Fig. 6.8 shows the essentials.

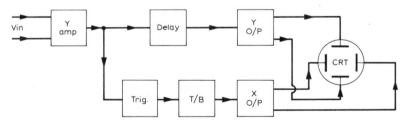

Fig. 6.8 Simplified block diagram to show how a Y signal delay permits the ramp time to start before the Y signal reaches the c.r.t.

Delay lines depend upon their operation upon the fact that the propagation speed of an electromagnetic signal in a cable is somewhat slower than in free air; in a co-axial cable it is about 0·6, and so it is possible to provide a small amount of signal delay without too much trouble, allowing the timebase a head start, as it were, before the Y signal actually reaches the c.r.t. In this way, much, if not all, of the waveform can be displayed, without any of the irritating losses that can occur with a timebase not aided by a Y signal delay. Delay lines can range from the modest printed circuit types that allow several hundred nS of delay, to more complex types that provide for longer delays. Alternative delay methods using dual timebases will be looked at later in the chapter.

The output from most timebases is insufficient to drive the c.r.t. directly, and so an intervening amplifier is necessary. Apart from amplifying the timebase output, the output amplifier has to provide a push-pull, or balanced output, since most c.r.t.'s are not too happy with single-ended (unbalanced) outputs. Unless designed specifically for single-ended work, most c.r.t.'s suffer from astigmatism and envelope distortion if fed from single-ended amplifiers.

Since a linear ramp is one of the priorities of 'scope design, it follows that the succeeding amplifier(s) must also be quite linear, and this calls for skill and care in design. However, since the bandwidth is severely restricted—in relation to the Y amplifier—this is an easier task than designing a perfectly linear Y amplifier.

Timebase repetition frequencies range from around 0·5S/cm to around 1$\mu$S/cm in even the simpler 'scopes, accompanied by the ability to slow the ramp down by a factor of around 2·5, and to speed it up by a factor of around $\times$ 10. In the better class of 'scope, an extension of at least $\times$ 5 is incorporated, extending the timebase repetition frequencies from around 2S/cm to around 200nS/cm.

## VERTICAL DEFLECTION

The principal task of the vertical amplifier is to accept very small input voltages and to amplify them to a point where they can exercise sufficient control over the deflector plates to position the spot over the area of interest. Modern c.r.t.'s are considerably more sensitive than their older counterparts, but input voltages, for a given deflection, are also tending to decrease, so the end-to-end gains are probably quite similar. In itself, this would not pose an insuperable problem, but bandwidth problems complicate matters somewhat. Rather like a Parkinson's Law, the more stages that are added to increase gain, the more the bandwidth decreases, and a high gain/bandwidth amplifier is a masterpiece of design.

Modern oscilloscopic techniques, and requirements, as outlined earlier, require that the Y signal is delayed for a period of time in order to give the timebase a head start. A delay line is therefore incorporated, usually between the preamp and the final output amplifier. The delay line in turn feeds the output amplifier.

## A.C. Coupled Vertical Amplifiers

An oscilloscope with an a.c. coupled amplifier exhibits an indifferent l.f. response, and this can be a distinct disadvantage when low frequency squarewaves have to be displayed. If we consider a squarewave with steeply rising and falling sides, (the faster the better) with flat horizontal portions, we have an ideal test waveform for many types of equipments, not least the 'scope to be used!

## Low Frequency Response

The slope of the horizontal portion of the squarewave is an indication of the low frequency capabilities of the 'scope, and of any other equipments involved, for instance hi-fi amplifiers. On a d.c. coupled 'scope the horizontals should be perfectly flat; on an a.c. coupled 'scope, i.e. using RC coupling between stages, considerable sagging may occur unless very large values of coupling capacitors are used and even then some sagging will still occur. This is occasioned by the coupling capacitors discharging and allowing the voltage to sag towards zero; the larger the capacitor used, the longer the discharge time and the flatter the horizontals for a given time.

## High Frequency Response

High frequency response is a function of stray capacitances, not only to earth, but also to earlier stages, where if the phase is 'correct' it tends to neutralise gain. This is shown in its essentials in Fig. 6.9.

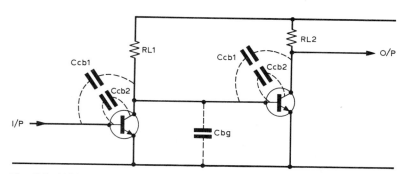

Fig. 6.9 Wideband amplification's enemies, stray capacitances: Cbg base to ground, Ccb1 base to emitter (external), Ccb2 base to emitter (internal).

Tr1 is influenced by strays to earth, strays between collector and base—both intrinsic and in the form of wiring. At the same time it is influenced by strays around Tr2, particularly those attributed to the much maligned Mr Miller, between base and collector, multiplied by the gain of Tr2. Very careful design is therefore necessary to obtain the required gain and bandwidth.

The gain of the vertical amplifier must be closely controlled, otherwise measurements cannot be made to any significant degree of accuracy. This requires stabilised power supplies, reasonably simple with transistored 'scopes, more difficult with valved 'scopes, but an additional cost irrespective of the devices used in the amplifier.

Earlier we saw that the deflection sensitivity was dependent upon the voltage on A3, and this means that the c.r.t. sensitivity is inversely proportional to the e.h.t. supplies; these in turn are also inversely proportional to the fluctuations in the mains supplies, and the cumulative effect in an area of wildly fluctuating mains will be appreciable. Apart from gain variations, supply variations will also cause the trace to float about, an additional source of irritation. Stabilised e.h.t. supplies are therefore desirable at best, mandatory where accuracy is important.

## The Complete Oscilloscope

So far, we have looked at the individual stages of an oscilloscope in a general, uncommitted sort of way. Now we can examine the instrument as a complete entity, and then go on to consider the individual stages again, this time in greater depth. The block diagram of a 'scope following well established practice is shown in Fig. 6.10. While incorporating a delay line, the configuration shown is essentially a very simple one; nevertheless, for non-specialist applications it is a very versatile one.

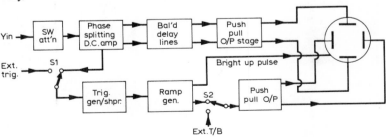

Fig. 6.10 Block diagram of inexpensive single beam oscilloscope with signal delay.

A switched attenuator precedes a wideband d.c. coupled amplifier. The attenuator is essential so that all inputs within wide limits can be attenuated to 'fit' the screen, without overloading the amplifier. The wideband amplifier then performs the amplification necessary to raise the lowest level signals, within the specification of the instrument, so that the best use is made of the c.r.t. window area. Direct coupling is used for the reasons outlined earlier; it also allows the magnitude of d.c. levels to be measured.

The output from the wideband amplifier is commonly push-pull, and so a balanced delay line is used, followed by another push-pull amplifier feeding the deflection plates.

Triggering from some types of waveforms can result in considerable jitter in the timebase, and so this is preceded by a trigger/ shaping circuit which accepts the triggering waveform and converts it into sharp 'spikes' that ensure that the timebase is triggered consistently and reliably. Modern timebases are a vast improvement on older timebases in this respect. Triggering can be from an internal signal or one from an external source, and S1 allows appropriate selection. An external timebase is sometimes desirable, and this can be selected by S2. The power supplies, not shown, are fully stabilised.

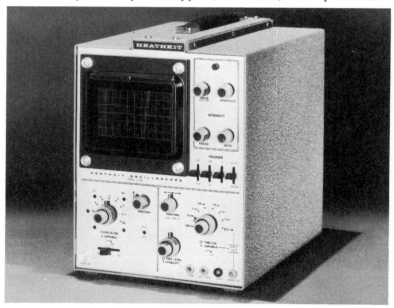

Fig. 6.11   Heathkit I0-103 triggered sweep oscilloscope possessing comprehensive facilities.

## THE VERTICAL AXIS

The first thing with which the waveform to be viewed comes into contact is the input attenuator. From Chapter 5 the reader will have deduced that there is rather more to attenuators than a casual glance might imply. With oscilloscopes, the problem is much more acute, since the bandwidth can extend from d.c.—no problem!—to many tens, sometimes hundreds, of MHz.

### Simple Attenuators

The very simplest attenuator takes the form of Fig. 5.2, with frequency compensation applied as in Fig. 5.4. and is commonly referred to as the stacked attenuator, for what will be obvious reasons.

It is a fairly primitive design in the attenuator heirarchy, but is sometimes used for non-critical applications. Even with very careful design and construction, it is unwise to rely on it much above the low r.f. range for the h.f. response is severely restricted.

### Compound Attenuators

A more elegant, and much used attenuator configuration is that shown in Fig. 6.12. This comprises a series of 'L' sections, each of fixed attenuation, independent of the next section, and fully frequency-compensated. The attenuation ratios are determined as outlined in Chapter 5, and the sequence may be 1-2-5 or 1-3-10.

The first position of the switch offers no attenuation, but R1 and R2 in series form the input load, typically 1 MΩ. The next position maintains the load unchanged, but now there will be either × 2 or × 3 attenuation inserted. Moving the switch along inserts additional attenuation, but the input resistance remains unchanged, and, if the frequency compensation capacitors are correctly adjusted, so does the input capacitance.

The rejection of d.c. is effected by C1; for the measurement of d.c. voltages, or of low frequency rectangular waveforms, where the presence of C1 would produce unacceptable sag, C1 can be shorted out by S1. The combination of C1, R2, forms an aperiodic filter, with R2 serving to limit the current the input device can draw when subjected to an overload.

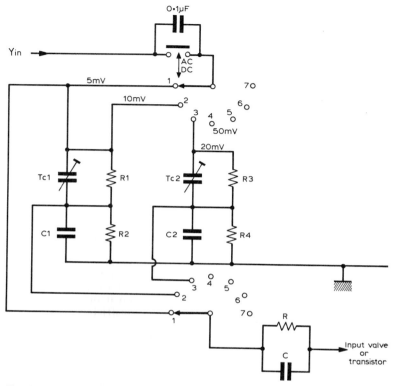

Fig. 6.12  Multiple L-section attenuator. Remaining switch connections are to further RC sections, similar to TC1, C1, R1, R2, but offering increasing attenuation.

## Cascade Attenuators

An alternative to Fig. 6.12 is to use a number of individual stages of, typically, $\div 10$, $\div 100$, and $\div 1000$, with fill-in stages of $\div 2$ and $\div 5$. These can then be used individually, or in combinations, or completely bypassed when the maximum gain is required, allowing a modest number of stages to provide a greater number of attenuation ratios.

For instance, an attenuator of the Fig. 6.12 type, covering from, typically, 5mV/cm to 20V/cm would require no less than 11 individual stages, remembering that the 5mV/cm position is straight through. By suitable switching, the same number of attenuation ratios can be obtained from just 5 stages. This configuration is therefore commercially very attractive, in spite of a more expensive switch (four poles instead of two).

## Split Attenuators

A derivation of the cascade attenuator follows the scheme shown in Fig. 2.12 where a primary, or coarse, attenuator precedes the input preamp, and is then followed by a secondary, or fine, attenuator. The two electrical sections are mechanically coupled. The coarse attenuators will be $\div 10$, $\div 100$, and $\div 1000$, and the fine attenuator will be $\div 2$ and $\div 5$.

Suitable switching then connects them in cascade, but with the buffering action of the preamp, so that, as with the cascade attenuator proper, all attenuation ratios from minimum—straight through—to the maximum provided can be obtained with a single rotary switch.

Whatever the circuitry adopted, two vital factors must be met. These are that the input resistance/capacitance must not alter from range to range, otherwise, clearly, the input signal will meet with differing input conditions from range to range, and may as a result suffer deformation and/or change of attenuation. Various artifices are adopted according to the attenuator configuration selected, and modern 'scopes are standardised with an input resistance of $1\text{M}\Omega$ in parallel with, typically, 28pF, though this capacitance may vary by around $-10$pF to $+20$pF.

## Frequency Compensation

The frequency compensating capacitors require considerable care in adjustment, otherwise the attenuator will not be truly aperiodic, essential for accurate wideband work, and will cause deformation of rectangular waveforms. The result of correctly and incorrectly adjusted frequency compensating capacitors is shown in the oscillogram of Fig. 6.13.

If a truly rectangular waveform is passed through a correctly adjusted frequency compensating capacitor, it will pass through unchanged, i.e. the leading and trailing edges are still perfectly square. Fig. 6.13, a multiple exposure oscillogram, shows, top trace, the undistorted leading edge of a fast, 250nS, squarewave. The middle trace shows the effect of over compensation, leading to overshoot, caused by an excessive amount of capacitance. The lower

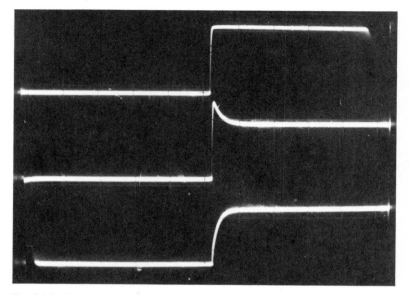

Fig. 6.13 Attenuator compensation. Top trace, as generated; centre trace, over-compensation; lower trace, under-compensation multiple-exposure.

trace shows the effect of undercompensation, leading to rounding off, caused by insufficient capacitance.

It is sometimes found that absolutely perfect compensation is not possible, but a waveform corresponding to Fig. 6.13 should certainly be possible. Failure to achieve a good waveform *may* be due to the dielectric of the capacitor(s) used altering slightly with frequency, and the only cure is to try alternative capacitors until the desired waveform is obtained.

## Attenuator Construction

Attenuator construction also poses problems. Indifferent screening may be the cause of hum pickup, or of signal breakthrough, particularly with very high gain amplifiers. The distribution of stray capacitances and inductances may cause resonances, and these in turn will cause 'suckouts' or peaks in the response curve, sometimes of quite serious proportions.

Well constructed attenuators are characterised by compact construction and short direct leads, reducing the stray capacitances and inductances to a minimum, and thereby ensuring that any resonances that do occur are well outside the intended bandwidth.

## Attenuator Resonances

The effect of attenuator resonance can be particularly acute when very fast pulses of the nS order have to be examined. Such pulses, with their wide ranging harmonic content, can excite a resonant attenuator and cause it to 'ring', an effect where the horizontal following the leading edge, consists of a train of oscillations, that decay more or less gradually to zero. This can present a totally misleading display and lead the unwary to seek non-existent faults in the equipment under investigation, whereas it was the 'scope that was at fault.

## Input Amplifiers

The output from the attenuator connects into an input preamp, which may be a valve—and these still found favour with designers well into the transistor era because of their considerable resistance to excessive voltage inputs, their other deficiencies being overlooked —or a transistor. These are now *the* chosen devices, most commonly FETs in the input stages. FETs are relatively fragile, and will not tolerate the sort of abuse and misuse that valves will, and therefore comprehensive protective circuits are very necessary.

## Valve Input Amplifiers

There are many excellent 'scopes where valves are used in some, or all, of the circuits, and so some knowledge of the principles involved is useful. Decoupling involving the conventional RC circuit has the disadvantage that it is not effective down to d.c. being dependent on the time constant of R × C. Very large values of R are impracticable due to the voltage lost across it; size and cost dictate the maximum value of C.

Decoupling down to d.c., essential for d.c.-coupled 'scopes, is not possible with the RC circuit. However, by connecting a transistor emitter-follower in the anode circuit of the valve, it is possible to provide decoupling down to d.c. The emitter current, which is the anode current of the valve, is determined by the relative values of the two base resistors.

## FET Input Amplifiers

The use of these as input devices is now virtually universal, and several advantages accrue from their adoption. Heater supplies, with their attendant problems of hum injection into sensitive circuits, are not necessary. Valves, though extremely abuse resistant, suffer from the possibilities of inter-pin leakages, inter-electrode leakages, and, possibly the most serious, suffer from ageing, whereby fairly frequent recalibration has to be effected if the 'scope is to be useful for accurate measurements. Microphony can also be a problem. These problems (now almost historical!) are worth mentioning, because they serve to emphasise the importance of the FET.

The FET is employed as a source-follower, with the output being extracted from across the source load resistor. The FET shares with the valve the characteristic of very high input resistance, and this is mainly dictated by the maximum resistance between gate and source the FET will tolerate without suffering excessive thermal drift; for 'scope work, this is customarily $1 M\Omega$ and little drift should occur.

Precision work demands zero drift, or compensation against drift, and so it is not uncommon to use two matched FETs, one for the input proper, the other purely for thermal compensation, but both connected as source followers. The gate of the second FET connects to a potential divider across the positive and negative supplies, and the source current can therefore be set to a given value.

Thermal drift in the input FET manifests itself as a vertical movement of the trace when the input attenuator is adjusted. Compensation takes the form of adjusting the gate voltage of the second FET such that the trace remains stable when the input attenuator is adjusted. The output from the FETs is balanced, and so balanced amplifiers are required throughout.

Overload protection is effected by diodes in conjunction with a current limiting series resistor; any voltage exceeding the bias on the diodes is safely shunted off to earth, so limiting the voltage reaching the gate to a magnitude within the FET maximum ratings, while voltages below the bias level are allowed to pass without let or hinder.

The effects of transistor input capacitance on bandwidth have been illustrated in Fig. 6.9, and a short exposition was also given. The use of FETs of the dual gate variety greatly reduces the input capacitance since these can be likened to two ordinary FETs in cascade, where the drain of one transistor forms the source load of the other.

The top earthed-gate transistor provides a low impedance at its source, and this forms the drain load for the lower earthed-source transistor. Because this is a very low collector load, very little signal is developed at the drain of the bottom transistor, effectively restricting it to a low gain, and therefore reducing the Miller effect to negligible proportions.

Since the FET is the first device in a chain of events, its characteristics dictate what happens along the chain, and since this is direct coupled any little change in the characteristics of the FET are magnified and exercise considerable control on the signal appearing on the screen. This is somewhat of a mixed blessing indeed.

Unwanted changes can be disastrous; on the other hand, the change in gain with change of current flowing can be usefully employed to counteract the effects of mains voltage variations. By varying the operating current of the FET proportionally with the mains voltage variations, it is possible to design an amplifier with virtually constant overall gain.

**Vertical Amplifiers**

Since most amplifiers are push-pull after the preamp, it is not uncommon for the main vertical amplifier to consist of stages of long-tailed pairs in cascade, and this has the considerable advantage of improving stability, since any change in one half is immediately counteracted by a change in the other half. The long-tail pair is

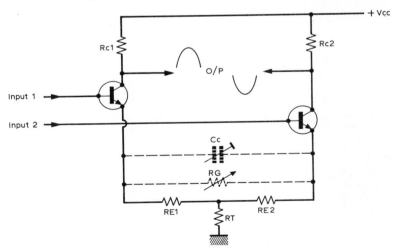

Fig. 6.14 An input to either base will provide anti-phase outputs from the two collectors. Cc provides frequency compensation and RG varies the gain.

shown in Fig. 6.14. Rc1 and Rc2 are the two collector loads, RE1 and RE2 provide negative feedback to improve stability and linearity, while RT sets the tail current.

Frequency compensation can be effected by a capacitor between the two emitters—shown dotted—while gain can be controlled by varying the negative feedback by means of a variable resistor, or switched fixed resistors connected between the two emitter resistors. This must cover the range between the 1-2-5-10 sequence to act as a fill-in control.

The long-tail pair possess the further merit of allowing a variable voltage to be connected to one of the bases—the signal connects to the other. This variable voltage then acts as a shift voltage, permitting the trace to be moved on the screen. The output signal is therefore a balanced one, in contrast to the input signal which was unbalanced.

## Bandwidth of Cascaded Amplifiers

Having cheerfully made the statement that an amplifier can consist of a number of long tailed pairs in cascade, we must now qualify that statement! The bandwidth of *any* amplifier is dependent upon the number of stages and their individual gains, so that we simply cannot obtain vast amounts of gain by means of cascaded amplifiers without paying any penalties. The penalty we have to pay is one of severely reduced bandwidth if we try for the gain we need with multitudinous stages. It simply isn't possible.

## Bandwidth and Rise Time

To explain why, we must digress a little and consider the implications of rise time in relation to bandwidth. While rise time is extremely important, anyway, it eases the task of explaining the problems of obtaining wide band gain with many stages! And I'm all in favour of easing what can, at times, become a very onerous task: the assimilation of knowledge.

Originally, oscilloscopes were designed for maximum bandwidth irrespective of transient response, but we have seen that the response to transient waveforms can be extremely important. So the original criteria for bandwidth, the 3dB or 0·707 points, are now obsolete, (this was the point at each end of the bandwidth where the response had fallen to 0·707 of its value mid-band) and different criteria are used to judge the performance of modern 'scopes. This is the time it takes for a step voltage, i.e. the leading edge of a rectangular or square waveform, to rise from 10% to 90% of its total value, the step rise time being the ideal, i.e. zero.

A close approximation between risetime and bandwidth is the formula $T = (350\text{--}400/F)$ nS. An amplifier with a bandwidth of 10MHz would have a risetime of 350–400/10 i.e. around 35 to 40nS. Conversely, an amplifier with risetime T, say 100nS, would have a bandwidth of 350–400/100 or 3·5 to 4MHz.

Having in a roundabout, but useful, way arrived at the definition of rise time, we can set about explaining how this enables us to calculate the response of a number of stages. Quite simply, it is this: The *overall* risetime of a number of amplifiers, or other devices, in cascade is given by $\sqrt{T1^2 + T2^2 + T3^2}$, and so on, depending on the number of stages involved.

So if we have two amplifiers in cascade with risetimes of $2\mu S$ and $6\mu S$, the overall rise time will be $\sqrt{2^2 + 6^2}$ or $6\cdot325\mu S$. Now, if the reader would like to do his own maths he can soon deduce the reduction in bandwidth of successive amplifiers, and this of course returns us to the long tailed pairs where we started off.

## Distributed Amplifiers

A successful attempt at getting round the limitations of frequency response reduction in cascaded amplifiers using valves was the transmission line or distributed amplifier, a configuration I used in my own home-made 'scope. Again, the reader may come into contact with instruments using this principle, so a short exposition is in order.

Fig. 6.15 shows the elements. In my own case, the top limit was 20MHz, but commercial 'scopes extended this to over 100MHz. The principle is fairly simple; the execution is somewhat more difficult! With valves, heat was a great problem where many were involved, so any reduction in their number was particularly welcome, and the attribute of the distributed amplifier of converting nearly all the h.t. into useful work was much appreciated.

Consider Fig. 6.15, and imagine that the anode voltage of the input preamp—not shown—suddenly changes; the voltage across RL will increase, say. This is impressed upon the line of inductors, L3, L4, L5, associated with the grid/cathode capacitances of V1, V2, V3. The propagation speed of this pulse is determined by the values of LC in the grid line. As the pulse passes each grid, a corresponding, magnified, pulse is generated at its anode.

Suppose V1 has a pulse at its anode. This can go one of two ways: 'left' or 'right'. If the impedance of the anode inductors is the same, the pulse splits into two, one half travelling each way. The 'left hand' pulse is absorbed by R1, the 'right hand' pulse travels along anode inductors L7, L8, L9. Provided these have been carefully balanced with the anode capacitances, the pulse will travel along, getting a boost at each anode.

We can think of the process as a pulse travelling along the anode line and getting a healthy boost at each anode, reaching the c.r.t. deflector plate, doing its work, *and then being reflected back along the line* until it in turn is absorbed by R1. Here is the crux of the matter, or at least one of them. *R1 must absorb the pulse completely*, or else it will recommence its travels, mixed up with subsequent pulses, and will be the cause of much doubt and anguish.

The grid excitation pulse, however, must not be reflected at all; if it was, the anodes would be sending out pulses in reverse order, and the display can well be imagined. To prevent reflection, the grid line must be terminated in the correct resistor value, and this is R2, at the end of the grid line.

The extra inductors, and trimmer capacitors, are included to ensure that the terminating resistors are truly aperiodic at the upper frequency limit of the amplifier. The delay lines for the distributed amplifier must be very carefully designed, built, and set up, otherwise at best the system will fail to perform its intended function, at worst it will become unstable, as mine did when I first tried it out.

### Vertical Output Amplifiers

With the distributed amplifier, all the valves contribute to the overall gain, so there are few problems in obtaining adequate scan. Other circuits are less sensitive, and the voltage handling capabilities of transistors are in the main somewhat limited. To obtain an adequate scan of even a modern sensitive, c.r.t., requires special output stages, a typical arrangement being that of Fig. 6.16.

Again, it is of the long tail configuration, with Tr1 and Tr2 being the long tail proper, and with constant current transistors Tr3 and Tr4 to reduce the loss that occurs when resistors are used in the emitter circuits. Gain control is effected by bridging the long tail emitters, by either a continuously variable resistor, or with a combination of variable and fixed preset resistors.

The continuously variable resistor acts as a fill-in control and the presets are adjusted to provide predetermined gains, typically $\times$ 1 and $\times$ 10. A capacitor to compensate for h.f. fall-off in gain is usually also included across the long tail emitters, sometimes aided by inductances in series with the collector resistor loads, RC.

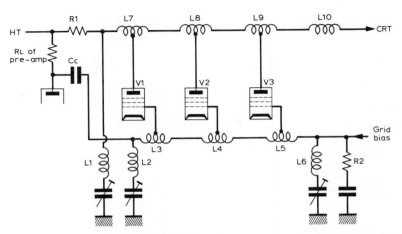

Fig. 6.15 Distributed amplifier. The preamp may follow the input attenuator or may follow a buffer cathode follower.

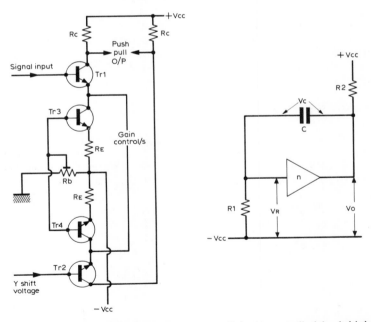

Fig. 6.16 (left) Long-tail pair output stage. Gain is controlled by bridging Tr1-Tr2 emitters. Signal input and Y shift are applied to Tr1-Tr2.

Fig. 6.17 (right) Miller integrator using an op-amp.

The advantage of the long tail pair is utilised here, with the input signal applied to one base, a shift voltage being applied to the other base. Emitter currents are set by the preset in the emitter circuit. Since fairly large voltage swings are required, high voltage transistors are used.

## THE HORIZONTAL AXIS

### Timebases

Unless an external timebase is being used, all the horizontal functions start with the timebase generator, so this is a good point to start our look at the horizontal axis. We saw earlier how the charging characteristic of a capacitor was utilised to provide a ramp voltage varying with time, and the importance of the ramp being perfectly linear.

Various circuits have been used; some are of no more than historical interest, others are still viable years after their discovery. They share a common aim: the provision of a linear ramp, though some are more successful than others. In essence, the effective time constant and charging voltage are artificially increased, enabling a comparatively small part of the ramp—where it is still linear—to be used.

### The Miller Integrator

The Miller effect can be a great problem at times. Here, it is utilised to provide us with a linear ramp, and is popularly known as the Miller-integrator. Fig. 6.17 shows the arrangement in a simplified op-amp manner. The capacitor C has across it a voltage, $V_c$, which is the sum of the voltage across the resistor R1 and the output voltage $V_o$, i.e. $V_c = V_r + V_o$. $V_o$, however, exceeds $V_r$ by the gain of the amplifier, call it n, and so $V_c$ is equal to $V_r(n + 1)$. Put another way, $V_r = \dfrac{V_o}{n+1}$.

When the voltage $V_o$ changes, the voltage across R1 will also change, by the ratio of $x/n + 1$ where x is the change in $V_o$. The capacitor charging current is therefore held almost constant, and an almost linear ramp is generated.

In practical terms, we can substitute a valve for the op-amp. If we take it for granted that C is fully charged, we can visualise the run-down. C begins to discharge via R2, and $V_o$ begins to decrease.

The grid begins to increase, towards h.t. The decreasing anode voltage, $V_o$ is trying to oppose the increasing grid voltage $V_r$, which was the cause of the whole process.

Providing the gain of the valve is large, the change in Vr need only be small, maintaining the voltage across R1, and hence the current in it, at an almost constant value, and this in turn is the discharging current in C. $V_o$ therefore decreases linearly, giving us the desired linear ramp. Effectively, we are making C aim at a voltage considerably in excess of the h.t.

So far we have generated our linear ramp and nothing else. To be useful and perform its intended task, the ramp must repeat itself continuously, either free-running or triggered. To do this, we must change from a triode to a pentode. A gating waveform applied to g3 will cause the anode to produce the linear ramp whilst g3 is about cathode potential. When the gate goes negative, the anode will start to cut-off and return towards h.t. A gating waveform is not always convenient, or desirable, and so the valve must be made self-oscillating, and this action is effected by the components associated with g2 and g3.

The Miller integrator in its basic form suffers from several deficiencies, of which the most severe is the steep transient when the valve is driven from cut-off into conduction, and this may result in a bright dot at the commencement of the trace. This can be suppressed fairly easily, and the Miller integrator is a very useful and versatile circuit.

Due to the fundamental difference between valves and transistors (impedance wise) the Miller integrator is better suited to valve circuitry. The Miller integrator can be modified to work with the low impedances associated with bipolar transistors, but there are alternative circuits which find favour increasingly with the wholesale adoption of transistors.

**Multivibrator Timebases**

An astable multivibrator is used as a timebase in some 'scopes. Here, a pair of transistors are coupled as a collector/base astable multivibrator as shown in Fig. 6.18. The timing capacitor $C_T$ is charged via Tr3. As the voltage on the emitter of Tr3 approaches the base voltage, Tr3 cuts-off and therefore drives Tr2 into conduction.

The charged capacitor will start to discharge through the constant current transistor Tr4, and the rate of discharge is now determined by the current flowing in Tr4, which in turn is dependent on the

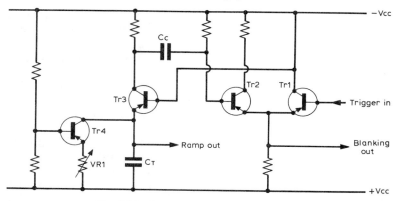

Fig. 6.18    Multivibrator timebase circuit.

base current flowing through the fine frequency control VR1. As $C_T$ discharges, a positive-going ramp is generated, and is in turn passed on to the power output stages.

Tr1 is the trigger input amplifier. The trigger pulse, normally derived from a squaring stage or from the indispensible Schmitt trigger, is applied to the base. A nice sharp pulse is required so that the timebase is kicked smartly into operation. Since the bases of Tr1 and Tr2 are coupled together, a common emitter current flows, and a pulse applied to Tr1 causes the emitter current of Tr2 to change in sympathy.

The receipt of a trigger pulse causes Tr2 to conduct, turning Tr2 off, and initiating the ramp just a shade prior to the point it would have done so anyway. The timebase is therefore synchronised to the trigger pulse, and as this is derived from the vertical amplifier correct synchronisation of the signal occurs.

Flyback blanking, which is sorely missed on lesser 'scopes that do not incorporate it, is effected by the pulse from the emitter of Tr1. Since this is positive-going, and for blanking we require a negative-going pulse on the c.r.t. grid, an inverting stage is required, and the pulse from this cuts-off the c.r.t. during the flyback.

The multivibrator timebase just described forms the basis of the timebase in the well known Heathkit 10-102 'scope.

### Bootstrap Timebases

A type of circuit popular for transistor timebases is the bootstrap, shown in its simplest elements in Fig. 6.19. To initiate the ramp, a

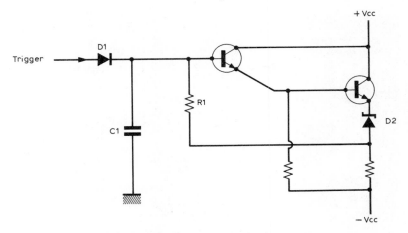

Fig. 6.19   The bootstrap timebase.

negative-going gating pulse is applied to drive the trigger hold-off diode D1 out of its non-conducting state. As soon as D1 begins to conduct, the timing capacitor C1 begins to charge through the timing resistor R1. The compound emitter followers TR1 and TR2 in conjunction with the zener diode D2 maintain a near constant voltage across R1, and the result is a near perfect negative going ramp at the emitter of TR2.

When the gating, or trigger, pulse ceases, D1 reverts back to its reverse biased, or non-conducting state and discharges C1, initiating the flyback. The quiescent state is then maintained until the arrival of the next trigger pulse, when the whole process is repeated. The spot sits at the left hand edge of the screen until called into action, and the process is essentially a monostable one.

**Emitter Coupled Timebase**

An emitter coupled timebase is shown in Fig. 6.21. This is so called because the timing capacitor is coupled between the emitters of Tr1 and Tr3. The ramp is initiated by a positive going pulse into the base of Tr1, through the trigger hold-off diode D1. Constant current charging is effected by Tr4, with the variable resistor in its base acting as a variable time control.

Time expansion is effected by selecting the appropriate resistor in Tr4 emitter; these are preset to the desired expansion. The timing capacitor $C_T$ is normally switched in decade ranges, and, typically,

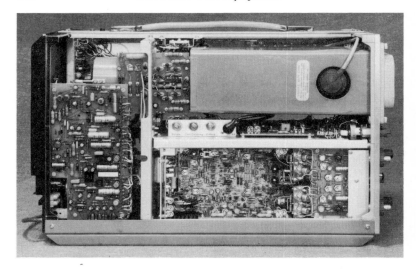

Fig. 6.20   Marconi TF2210 oscilloscope with cover removed.

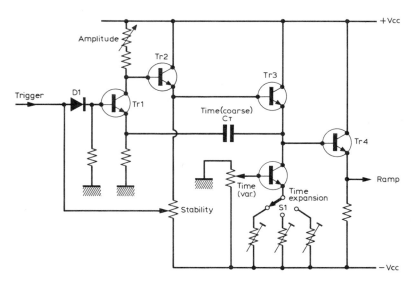

Fig. 6.21   Emitter coupled timebase, showing essentials.

would provide ranges of 10mS/cm to 100nS/cm, with the necessary expansion being selected by S1, and this would be in the 1-2-5 sequence, with 1-3-10 as an alternative.

The range of the variable time control would be selected to just 'fill-in' the gaps. With time expansion, the overall range would be from 50mS/cm to 500nS/cm, or from 100mS/cm to 1μS/cm. S1 can, of course, be coupled to the switch used for the selection of $C_T$, and would then automatically provide the full range of sweep speeds.

**Timebase Frequency/Linearity**

The necessity for a perfectly linear timebase ramp has been emphasised, with justification, on several occasions. However, a 'scope that is linear on one range may not necessarily remain linear on its other ranges as Fig. 6.22 shows.

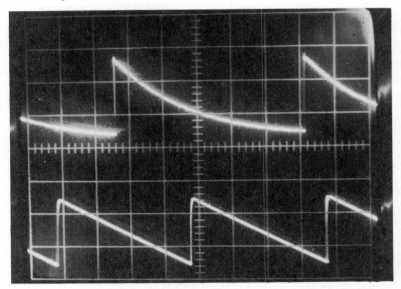

Fig. 6.22   Showing severe non-linearity at a low timebase repetition frequency and the improvement at a higher frequency. Upper trace, 50mS/cm; lower trace, 0·1mS/cm. Multiple exposure.

This is a *multiple* exposure and shows, top trace, the ramp operating at a low repetition frequency, where large values of timing capacitor are required. The lower trace shows the ramp at a considerably faster repetition frequency, where smaller values of timing capacitor are required, The timebase speeds of the viewing 'scope were 50mS/cm and 0·1mS/cm respectively, the vertical scale being 20V/cm.

### Horizontal Output Amplifiers

Horizontal output amplifiers, in general, tend to follow the pattern established by the vertical output amplifier. However, it will be recollected, the sensitivity of the horizontal plates of a c.r.t. is much less than that of the vertical plates, a position rendered just a little bit more difficult by the extra scan required; 10cm against 8cm for the vertical on a nominal 25cm c.r.t.

If the bandwidth was required to be equivalent to that of the vertical amplifiers, then the problems would be much more severe. Fortunately, a much reduced bandwidth is adequate, as can be seen from the following explanation. If we suppose that the maximum sweep velocity is $1\mu S$/cm, then the complete 10cm sweep will occupy $10\mu S$, and the reciprocal of this gives us the frequency, which is 100kHz.

For many applications such a bandwidth would suffice, but it is common to provide a wider bandwidth than the nominal minimum, not least because many 'scopes provide for an expansion of $\times$ 5 or $\times$ 10, increasing the sweep speed to around 200nS/cm to 100nS/cm, and, clearly, the horizontal amplifier must be able to cope with this increased speed.

There is also the occasional requirement for an external timebase, whatever the frequency or waveform, and as a consequence most good quality general purpose 'scopes have horizontal amplifiers with a response extending to between 500kHz and 2MHz.

### Triggering the Timebase

To synchronise a timebase so that a stable display is obtained, it is necessary to inject a signal from the vertical amplifier to start the timebase off at precisely the right moment, and on older 'scopes the timebase was adjusted to be fractionally slower than required, the 'sync' control being adjusted to obtain a stationary trace. At times this could be a time consuming task, and on some 'scopes proper sync was difficult, if not impossible, to obtain.

A much better method is to definitely trigger the timebase, to kick it vigorously into action, so that as the variable time control is adjusted, the cycles either add themselves onto the end of the display, or remove themselves from it, with no meaningless conglomeration of lines in between. Anyone who has used a modern triggered 'scope would not willingly go back to the old system.

To trigger a timebase it is still necessary to derive a signal from the vertical amplifier. This signal should be variable so that the timebase can be triggered from a selected point on the waveform to be displayed, and from an a.c. signal from a selected polarity. This is not only easier but is much more precise if the vertical signal is not used 'raw', but is suitably processed. To do this it must be converted into a series of constant width pulses with sharp edges. The timebase is then decisively kicked into operation, instead of being gently persuaded.

### The Schmitt Trigger

A popular way of obtaining the required pulses is to shape them by the use of the indispensible Schmitt trigger circuit or bi-stable. The action of this was discussed in Chapter 3, and so little need be said of it now. In the simpler Schmitt triggers, dual polarity triggering is obtained by extracting the anti-phase outputs from the collector—or anode—load resistors. Variable triggering level is effected by either preceding the trigger with a buffer amplifier with a gain control, or by making the resistor in the second base—or grid—variable. In both cases, the level at which the trigger changes state is altered, and this level can be selected to coincide with a particular part of the vertical waveform.

A somewhat more elaborate, and generally more precise, circuit is that of Fig. 6.23. Here, a long tail pair is used to provide dual polarity triggering, as well as acting as a trigger level control for the following Schmitt trigger stage. Since direct coupling is used between the long tail pair and the trigger, the output to the trigger will be proportional to the difference between the voltage levels at the long tail pair bases.

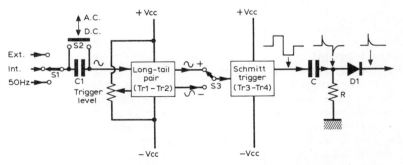

Fig. 6.23 Block diagram of dual polarity variable level trigger stage. If D1 is reversed, the output will be negative-going.

If the hysteresis voltage of the trigger is reduced to suitably low levels, the trigger will change state every time the level of the input voltage equals (almost) the voltage present at the wiper of the trigger level control. Since the trigger level control is connected between the positive and negative supplies, a precise control of triggering in both the positive and negative directions is effected. With dual polarity supplies there is no problem.

With single polarity supplies, the bias applied to Tr1, Tr2, can be selected such that the bases and emitters sit somewhere between $+$Vcc and $-$Vcc to allow a reasonable range of dual polarity triggering since the base bias of Tr2 can be taken below that of Tr1 which is fixed by the potential divider.

The output from the trigger goes to a differentiating network comprising C and R, the time constant of which must be carefully selected to provide pulses of the correct width. Since dual polarity pulses will completely baffle the timebase generator, one of them must be removed, and this function is effected by a series diode D1; depending on the way D1 faces, either the positive or the negative pulse will be passed on, but not both.

The input to the long tail pair is usually an a.c. signal derived from the vertical amplifier. For some applications an external triggering source is essential (sometimes a mains frequency signal must be used) and so a source selector switch is included. This is S1.

Switches S1, S2, and S3 may be separate, mechanically, in which case they are frequently of the 'key' or 'lever' type; occasionally, in low cost 'scopes, slider switches are used. They can also be used in combination, in which case mechanical coupling is used so that a single rotary knob can be used to select all the functions provided, electrical switching being effected by a series of multi-way multipole switch wafers.

## Low Frequency Triggering

For triggering from very low frequencies, the coupling capacitor, C1, must be short circuited (by S2) and Tr1 is fed directly, together with any d.c. voltage that may be present. This enables triggering to be effected, but at a price. The removal of the coupling capacitor, and the impression of a d.c. signal on the base of Tr1 removes the symmetrical triggering formerly possible. However, a pre-set resistor is usually provided to enable a zero output signal to be obtained under these conditions, when the trace is in the centre of the screen, and this means that, with internal triggering, the trigger level control range is symmetrical about the centre of the screen.

## Low Frequency Rejection

It is also desirable, at times, to trigger from a high frequency signal riding, i.e. superimposed, upon a low frequency signal, without the timebase trying to trigger from both signals. This is effected by interposing a high-pass filter in the signal path—sometimes nothing more elaborate than a lower value of interstage coupling capacitor is used. The value of such a capacitor is clearly a compromise between low frequency rejection and high frequency admittance.

## High Frequency Triggering

In some of the older 'scopes difficulties in making the Schmitt 'trigger' properly at h.f. resulted in indifferent triggering and an unstable display. The effect was—is—particularly pronounced with sinewaves due to the—comparatively—leisurely manner in which they rise and decay, and triggering deteriorated markedly as the signal frequency increased. A partial solution was to bypass the trigger and feed the input straight into the timebase where it effected a measure of synchronism.

## Auto Triggering

Manual triggering has undoubtedly advantages for the experienced user, to whom the polarity and precise triggering level *may* be all-important. On the other hand, the polarity and triggering level may not be critical, the principal requirement being a stable display. For the inexperienced user, the disappearance of the trace with an insufficient trigger voltage level, or absence of the triggering signal, may be a cause of considerable worry since he will not know that this is a perfectly normal occurance, not in any way connected with his use of the 'scope.

Many 'scopes now incorporate the facility of switching the triggering to Auto, the trigger level control being switched out of operation. When this is done, the trigger bistable runs at an arbitrary, usually very low, frequency, and a trace is visible at all times, irrespective of the presence of any input.

If a signal is now applied, and providing its frequency is higher than that of the free-running bistable, this will be triggered every time the input signal changes state around the zero level. This provides automatic triggering, a small penalty being that the signal must be higher than the free-run frequency of the bistable. The trace is visible irrespective of the timebase repetition frequency.

### Bright Line Auto (Auto Fast)

Although a trace is visible in the Auto mode, the very low natural frequency of the bistable means a reduction in brilliance at higher timebase repetition frequencies. One way of overcoming this particular problem is to increase the natural frequency of the bistable very considerably—hundreds of kHz or more. When a trigger signal is applied, the bistable is changed into a monostable, producing an output pulse for every cycle of the trigger signal.

The simplification obtained on Auto is of real assistance for many applications where precisely defined triggering is neither essential or desirable. For other applications, the Auto mode can be an embarrassment, principally due to the fact that triggering is now effected at around zero volts.

If we take the example of a signal of varying amplitude around the zero base line, we can see that the trigger will be set a pretty insoluble problem. It will trigger the timebase each time the varying amplitudes cross the zero base line, and the result is likely to be an amalgamation of the various amplitudes on the trace, not at all what we wanted! By switching to one of the manual trigger modes, the precise triggering level can be selected and the trace will show what we really wanted all along.

### Tunnel Diode Triggering

The ubiquitous Schmitt trigger is not without failings, of which the chief is the difficulty of ensuring reliable triggering at high frequencies and we have already seen that some of the older 'scopes could be switched to the so-called h.f. triggering. This was all very well when 'scopes with a bandwidth of a few tens of MHz could be tolerated because there was nothing better. Now there is, and reliable h.f. triggering, proper triggering, is expected. The more sophisticated 'scopes use the tunnel diode as the trigger element, and while a detailed study is not possible due to lack of space, a brief look at the possibilities of the tunnel diode certainly is.

The characteristic curve is shown in Fig. 6.24. The unique property of this device lies along the line between $V_p$ $I_p$ to $V_v$ $I_v$. The *peak point forward current* $I_p$ is the value of the current at which the slope of the current-voltage curve changes from positive to negative, with *increasing voltage*.

The *valley-point current* $I_v$ is the current at which the slope of the current-voltage curve changes back to positive with increasing voltage. The relationship between $I_p$ and $I_v$ is most important, for

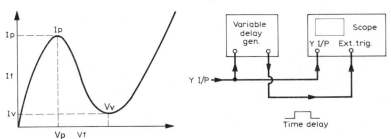

Fig. 6.24 (left) The characteristic curve of a tunnel diode, showing the 'negative resistance' between Vp and Vv.

Fig. 6.25 (right) An oscilloscope triggered by an external add-on variable delay generator.

it determines the current swing and hence the switching characteristics of any given device. Typical ratios are 10:1 for germanium devices, and 20:1 for gallium-arsenide devices. The *peak voltage* $V_p$ and the *valley voltage* $V_v$ are the points at which the peak current and valley current, respectively, occur.

Fig. 6.26 Author's home-built oscilloscope using a 6″ c.r.t. Bandwidth to 20MHz at 100mVcm p-p. It is heavy and cumbersome, but the large screen area is a delight!

So much, very briefly, for the device as such, but what can it actually do? Depending on circuit configurations, it can act as a monostable, bistable, or astable, with the very attractive merits of extremely fast switching times with low inherent noise levels. As such they are ideally suited to trigger circuits of all kinds, and can provide stable triggering from low level h.f. signals. All the trigger circuits we have looked at, and most others as well, can be usefully replaced by tunnel diode triggers.

Initially the devices were expensive and were therefore used in high quality 'scopes only, but with the fall in all semiconductor prices it is very likely that their uses will increase.

## OTHER TIMEBASES

This somewhat non-committal heading includes some very important timebase derivatives and variations, without which the 'scope would be very much less versatile. Of these, the most important is the delayed sweep, whereby a small portion of an overall picture, or a single event from a series of identical events can be picked out for individual examination.

### Delayed Sweeps

The classic problem used for the explanation of delayed sweeps is that of a single pulse that must be resolved and expanded while ignoring a series of identical pulses. Since it can be a very important practical problem, it is worth examining in a little detail. Let us suppose that a string of pulses are involved, each 1mS wide, with 5mS between them. To pick out any single pulse for examination is a formidable task, so let us cheat—just a little!—and put in convenient marker pulses in, say, every tenth position. Let us cheat just a little more and make the amplitude of the marker pulses somewhat greater than the standard pulses.

We now have a 'milestone', a point of reference, and this eases our task greatly. The standard pulses are 1mS wide, and so to completely fill the screen with such a pulse—assuming a 10cm screen—we require a sweep the duration of which occupies 1mS, or a sweep repetition frequency of $0 \cdot 1 \mu S/cm$. This will fill the screen with our required pulse, but how do we identify it?

To identify our pulse, we require a delay, and this is connected as in Fig. 6.25. The 'scope is triggered by the delayed pulse from the delay generator, and by selecting a suitable sweep speed the pulse can be expanded to the desired width, and of course the previously selected time delay enables the correct pulse to be picked out, the delay generator being triggered from a marker pulse prior to the pulse of interest.

The method has the merit of being simple and reliable, but is not particularly easy to use. Some juggling with the delay time and the sweep time is inevitable, and care and experience are required for reliable operation. For this reason, alternative methods have been developed, of which the dual timebase is now universally adopted. This can be used individually or in cascade.

### Dual Timebases

In its simplest form, the dual timebase configuration is as shown in Fig. 6.27. The main timebase is provided with the usual range of

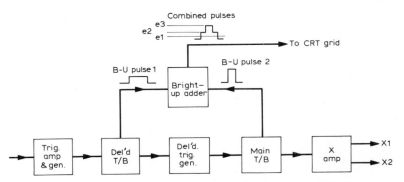

Fig. 6.27 Showing how the cut-off c.r.t. (point e1) is brightened up by pulse 1 (point e2) and then further brightened up by pulse 2 (point e3).

sweep speeds, and the delayed timebase is usually provided with a similar range of sweep speeds. The main timebase is frequently designated the 'A' sweep, the delay sweep being the 'B' sweep. On the more sophisticated 'scopes, the whole waveform—in our case the series of pulses—is displayed on the A sweep, and the portion of interest is displayed on the B sweep suitably expanded. Various modes are provided as explained below, appropriate switching then enables the desired mode to be selected.

When the variable delay mode is selected, the B sweep ramp generator is triggered from the A ramp, the precise trigger point being selected by a continuously variable *cm delay* control. If the A + B control is effective, the waveform consists of the normal waveform, with a brighter portion indicating the duration of the **B** sweep, and the *relative* brilliances of these two waveforms can be adjusted to emphasise the importance of either. Fig. 6.28 shows the appearance of the display. If the display switch is set to **B**, the **B** ramp is applied to the deflection circuit and the brightened portion is expanded to fill the screen.

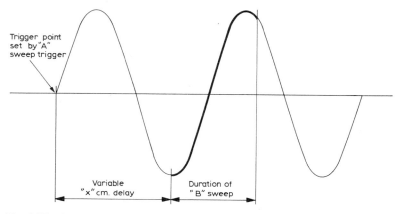

Fig. 6.28    Appearance of trace when timebase A is intensified by timebase B.

Reverting back to Fig. 6.27, we can see how the relative amplitudes of the two bright-up pulses effect the brightened portion of the **B** sweep. The cut-off tube is supplied with a bright-up pulse while the ramp is in motion and so displays the waveform applied to the c.r.t. by the deflection circuits. If the waveform is stepped, as in our case now, the c.r.t. is brightened-up for the normal trace, and then brightened-up again for the delayed trace.

### Single Shot Timebases

Some of the more sophisticated 'scopes incorporate a timebase which provides a single sweep on being triggered and which precludes the timebase being triggered again until manually reset. Such a feature is invaluable for random phenomena (pulses) but requires photographic assistance for any but the very slowest of pulses to be successfully deciphered.

The trigger circuit must be manually primed, and in the case of very infrequent pulses this can be a very trying affair, since the precise triggering point will be difficult to establish. Once the trigger pulse has started the timebase, the trigger hold-off diode is inhibited by the recycling action of the ramp generator. The diode remains inhibited until manual priming is again initiated.

The priming switch is also provided with a manual firing position so that the sweep can be manually initiated in the absence of a suitable trigger switch, and this can prove useful under conditions where manual triggering is acceptable.

## Dual Trace Operation

Although dual trace vertical channels are not, strictly speaking, part of the horizontal functions, they are in one instance influenced by the sweep generator so it is appropriate to consider them now. Before doing so, it is useful to clarify nomenclature. *Dual trace* 'scopes are understood to be instruments where electronic means are used to provide the dual channels, whilst *dual beam* 'scopes are understood to be instruments where completely seperate electron beam systems are used to provide the dual channels. Dual trace operation is effected by one of two means: *alternate* or *chopped*. Since the sweep generator is involved in the alternate mode, this will be considered next.

## Alternate Mode

In the alternate mode an electronic beam switch is employed, and is actuated by the sweep generator so that each channel is swept in turn. The electronic switch requires a pulse coincident with the end of each sweep, and this can be derived from the end of the bright-up pulse or from a pulse from the timebase, again coincident with the end of each sweep.

A differentiating network followed by a diode clipper similar to that of Fig. 6.23 triggers a bistable which drives the electronic switch, and this in turn alternately allows each channel to be passed onto the main Y amplifier, in the meantime cutting-off the unwanted channel.

The alternate sweep mode, at first sight the ideal solution to the problems of economical dual channel provision, suffers from two basic limitations which curtail its usefulness. These are flicker at slow sweep speeds, and phase differences between channels.

At even moderately slow sweep speeds the alternate switching causes flicker and this will clearly be a source of some operator discomfort, ultimately resulting in eye-strain. At slow sweep speeds the alternate switching may have a hypnotic effect, and considerable personal discomfort will result—the effects of 'stroboscopic' or repetitive light flashes are known to induce epilepsy in persons prone to the malady. For this reason, most 'scopes permit the sweep generator to be switched to the chop mode, either automatically below—commonly—1mS/cm, or manually, in which case the operaator must decide the switching change-over point.

The time taken for channel switching is finite, causing interchannel phase relationships to be lost, so this mode is of little use when reliable relative-phase measurements must be made.

**Chopped Mode**

In the chop mode the channels are still swept in turn but at a considerably increased rate, switching speeds ranging from 100kHz to 1MHz. In its simplest form, switching is effected by a beam switch bistable which also doubles up as the alternate mode switch by appropriate choice of bias levels. A single pair of transistors can be biased to perform as an astable multivibrator free-running at some high frequency within the limits given above, or as a bistable that changes states when triggered by the timebase to perform the alternate function.

The effect of the switching waveform is shown in Fig. 6.29. The two signals occupy the horizontal portions of the switching squarewave, the vertical transitions of which are extremely rapid and do not show on the display.

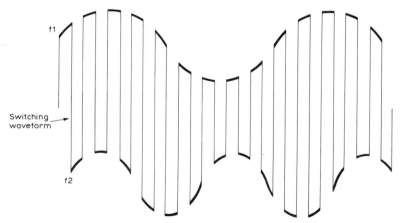

Fig. 6.29 Showing how two traces are obtained when in the chop mode.

Triggering in the chop mode must be made prior to the channel switch, for the switching waveform is just the right shape to take over control of the triggering if attempts are made to trigger from the composite signal. If the timebase *is* triggered by the switching waveform a stationary display will not be obtainable. Triggering from either of the signals will provide a stationary display, but both waveforms will not be stationary unless both have the same frequency.

The advantage of the chop mode is that phase relationships are not lost. A disadvantage is that if the sweep speed is increased appropriately the switching waveform may become visible providing a display similar to Fig. 6.29. Due to the random phase relationship between the input signals and the switching waveform, it is unlikely that the latter will be seen clearly unless used to trigger the timebase. A sparkling effect *may* be visible however. This is one reason why most 'scopes switch automatically to alternate at sweep speeds of around 1mS/cm and greater.

## POWER SUPPLIES

The power requirements of transistor 'scopes lie within the range of 15 to 30 volts, positive and negative, for the input amplifiers and sweep generators, though there are, as always, exceptions to the rule requiring higher positive voltages. The output amplifiers require between 150 to 250 volts depending on the drive required for the c.r.t. All these supplies are provided by conventional means, and may or may not be stabilised, since skilled circuit design can to some extent compensate for mains voltage variations.

The areas of particular interest in the power supply section are those relating to the provision of the p.d.a. and grid/cathode supplies, and these can span nearly a decade. For instance, the p.d.a. potential can range from a minimum of $+1.5$kV to at least $+15$kV, while the grid/cathode potentials can range from a minimum of some $-300$ volts to $-3$kV. The p.d.a. current is measurable in a few tens of $\mu$A, the grid current is zero, and the cathode current is only a very few mA.

The sensitivity of the c.r.t. is dependent on the voltage applied to the A3 anode, and this must be stabilised for reliable time and voltage measurements. The voltage on the grid, relative to the voltage on the cathode, determines the brilliance of the trace, and to some extent the size of the trace, and so ideally this too must be stabilised. The p.d.a. voltage has less influence on c.r.t. sensitivity than the other potentials, so this can escape stabilisation. However, the methods used to stabilise the remaining e.h.t. voltages frequently mean that the p.d.a. is also stabilised.

### Mains Derived E.H.T.

The least expensive way of obtaining the e.h.t. supplies is possibly from a mains transformer having the required secondaries, and this is potentially the most lethal way of doing so! For instance, a single 1kV winding will provide some 1·4kV of e.h.t. using simple half wave rectification, since the rectified d.c. voltage will almost equal the a.c. voltage $\times \sqrt{2}$ with only a lightly loaded bleeder network feeding the focus and brilliance controls. This will, in all probability, be smoothed by a capacitor of at least 0·1$\mu$F, possibly much higher, and the charge on this of $\frac{1}{2}CV^2$ will be sufficient to give a nasty shock and possibly burn into the bargain since the overall impedance is frighteningly low.

The p.d.a. voltage *may* be derived from the same winding by means of voltage doubling, trebling, or even quadrupling. The capacitors involved in the multiplying/smoothing network will be around 0·1$\mu$F, and while the impedance is higher due to the added components between the mains transformer secondary and the final output voltage, the capacity for damaging the incautious finger is still considerable.

Stabilisation of e.h.t. supplies has taken the form of a number of low voltage (around 70V) neons in series across the supply to be stabilised, and this scheme has the great merit of simplicity and low cost, but is only really effective where the load current is low in relation to the neon current. A similar scheme, and in keeping with the semiconductor philosophy, would be to use a number of Zener diodes in series, and since the voltage/current capabilities of these is much higher than that of the neons, they would be more effective.

A much more elegant, and more effective, but still comparatively simple circuit comprises a d.c. controlled a.c. bridge, where a transistor at the earthy end of the e.h.t. winding controls the voltage developed across the bridge, and hence the overall e.h.t. Since the p.d.a. is commonly developed from the same winding via voltage multiplication this is also stabilised.

### R.F. Power Supplies

An r.f. power supply consists of a power oscillator—which may be a valve—operating between some 20kHz and 50kHz. A transformer is used to supply the required e.h.t. supplies via two or more secondaries; one each for the grid and cathode, a third for the p.d.a. For simplicity, one winding may have to suffice for the grid and cathode, with the p.d.a. being derived via voltage multiplication from the same winding, or this may have an over-winding. Whatever the winding permutations principles are the same. Positive feedback is introduced from the tapped primary to induce, and then maintain, oscillations. To ensure that the output remains constant, a negative feedback loop is introduced by way of the e.h.t. secondary. Since the potential here is high, an attenuator is required.

The error voltage which is compared by the error amplifier against a built-in standard—zener or neon—is reduced proportionally, and so the amplifier performs an additional function—that of amplifying the *difference* between the standard voltage and the error voltage, and this forms the negative feedback voltage. To compensate for very slow output variations, the error amplifier must be d.c. coupled throughout.

The transformer will almost always be ferrite cored for maximum efficiency, and this determines the operating frequency. Older 'scopes used thermionic valves and/or 'metal' rectifiers. Modern 'scopes use silicon diodes almost exclusively, a number being used in series for the e.h.t. Smoothing will be by way of paper capacitors; these become expensive when a high capacity/voltage rating is required, and a number of series connected electrolytic capacitors may be used if economy is important.

In this respect, r.f. power supplies are more economical than mains derived supplies, due to the familiar capacitive reactance effect. Since the reactance of a capacitor is inversely proportional to frequency, it follows that for a given ripple level the capacitance values can be halved each time the frequency is doubled. Vacuum impregnation of the transformer is highly desirable, partly to reduce audible whistles, mainly to prevent leakages and flashovers.

## CHOOSING AN OSCILLOSCOPE

The pitfalls that await the intending purchaser of electronic test equipments pale into insignificance when compared to those awaiting the intending purchaser of a 'scope. There are two basic reasons for this. The first is purely financial, for the instrument can represent a very large and very real slice of investment, and therefore much more thought must be given to choosing one than to almost any other piece of test equipment. This begets the idea that a 'scope must be chosen to last for 'x' number of years, at first sight a most commendable idea. This brings us to the second reason.

If we decide that we want a 'scope with certain capabilities, we then look 'x' years into the future and endeavour to guess what our requirements will be in that time, and we purchase one which we think will suit. Inevitably, progress defeats us, for long before our 'x' number of years have expired, a whole new generation of instruments has arrived that will do all that we tried to forsee, and, infuriatingly, do it a jolly sight better! (of course this applies to some other instruments also).

The professional engineers, the men in industry, fare somewhat better than the unfortunate amateur or small businessman, for they have apprentices and trainees who can cut their electronic teeth on the 'scopes discarded by their more erudite seniors as being unworthy of their use. But there is a ray of hope for the amateur or small business man. If chosen wisely an oscilloscope will not become obsolete as quickly as the professional's—he *must* remain at the forefront *all* the time while they can follow at a more leisurely rate—and in many instances a second-hand 'scope rejected by the professional will still fulfill their requirements.

Starting with the vertical axis, we have to resolve two very important parameters: bandwidth and sensitivity.

### Audio Frequency Bandwidth

For purely a.f. work, i.e. from around 20Hz to 20kHz, a bandwidth extending up to at least 500kHz is essential. This will enable fast—$\simeq\mu$S—risetimes to be measured without loss of what may well be vital information. At the bottom end, the bandwidth must extend to d.c.

Such a 'scope will enable l.f. squarewaves to be measured without the infuriating, and measurement negating, sloping of the horizontals that is the characteristic of any equipment with an inadequate l.f. response. Moreover, it will enable the 'scope to be used as a d.c. volt or current (via shunts) meter of moderate accuracy and input resistance—3% to 5% and 1MΩ.

### General Purpose Bandwidth

For general purpose work a greatly extended bandwidth is essential. In keeping with the approach adopted earlier, bandwidth requirements will be explained in terms of risetimes. The 'bandwidth narrowing' effect we looked at on page 149 shows that the risetime of the 'scope must be appreciably faster if the input risetime is not to be 'stretched' to a point where it becomes meaningless. If we know the risetime of the fastest waveform we are likely to be involved with, and we know just how much stretching we can tolerate, then we can calculate the total bandwidth the 'scope should possess. An example might clarify matters, so here it is.

Let us assume that the risetime of the input waveform, call it $r_i$, is 50nS, and that we can tolerate an artificial 'stretching' of this—on the 'scope's screen—of 10%, call it $r_s$, we can now calculate the total bandwidth required of the 'scope, call it $r_o$, by means of the simple formula: $r_o = \sqrt{r_s^2 - r_i^2}$. Substituting our figures we get: $\sqrt{55^2 - 50^2} = 23nS$. The bandwidth is given by: 350 to 400/23 or some 15MHz to 17MHz. This is, by contemporary standards, a modest bandwidth, but it will, of course, be extended if we decide to work to a more stringent accuracy, say 5%, or if the risetime of the input waveform is much faster.

The formula above, simple though it is, enables the reader to carry out his own calculations, on the basis of his own requirements, and to arrive at a figure which will be his own 'goodness-factor'. Again, as with the purely a.f. 'scope, the bandwidth should extend down to d.c.

Having resolved the problems of bandwidth, we can now examine the requirements of sensitivity.

**Sensitivity**

In multimeter terminology, the sensitivity is expressed in terms of the series resistor necessary for the meter to read f.s.d. with 1 volt applied, i.e. 20kΩ/V. With 'scopes, a somewhat similar situation exists: this time the voltage necessary to deflect the trace by 1cm.

Since an a.c. sinewave can have three different magnitudes, dependent on the applied criteria—Vrms, Vpk, and Vp-p—it is vitally necessary to know which particular magnitude the 'scope is actually calibrated in, since Vrms = 0·707 Vpk, Vpk = $\sqrt{2}$ × Vrms, and Vp-p = 2 × $\sqrt{2}$ Vrms. These can thus be a difference of 2·8:1 if Vrms is compared to Vp-p, and the margin of error can be seen to be appreciable if the magnitude of the calibrating voltage is not known.

Some manufacturers are guilty of causing uncertainty by failing to state the input voltage necessary for a given deflection in the proper magnitude, and that is the voltage peak-to-peak necessary for 1cm deflection. It matters little if the graticule is scaled in Cubits or CentiCubits so long as the voltage is specified!

## Audio Frequency Sensitivity

For a.f. work the 'scope should have a sensitivity of at least 1mV/cm, and this should suffice to enable the minute output voltages from pickups and tapeheads to be analysed in reasonable detail. If the 'scope available does not have adequate sensitivity it is possible to use an external amplifier of the Fig. 2.14 type which is followed by a common emitter transistor with the values of collector load and emitter resistor adjusted for the required gain, bearing in mind that the gain of such a stage is approximately given by: R1/re or more accurately by R1/Re + re. where R1 is the collector load, re is the intrinsic emitter resistance, and Re is the external emitter resistor.

Alternatively, where only a single channel can be used, many dual trace 'scopes can be used in cascade, i.e. the two vertical channels are used in series, to provide an increased gain of, typically, × 5, at a roughly proportionally reduced bandwidth.

## General Purpose Sensitivity

General purpose 'scopes of only a few years ago were typified by sensitivities of around 100mV/cm. This has increased dramatically, and contemporary 'scopes offer between 5mV/cm and 10mV/cm, with the former probably being the most common. Depending upon the application, it will be clear that a reduced sensitivity *may* well prove quite acceptable.

It may prove interesting to note—in passing—that my own home-made 'scope shown stripped during modification in Fig. 6.26, has a maximum sensitivity of only 100mV/cm and that only infrequently do I regret the lack of an increased sensitivity. Of course, if the 'scope of your choice has a sensitivity greater than you require, you will just have to grin and bear it!

## Minimum Sensitivity

Most manufacturers are pleased to tell you the lowest voltage that their respective 'scopes will display, and of course this is an essential piece of information. What they do not always tell, probably unwittingly, is the minimum sensitivity, i.e. the maximum voltage the 'scope will accept before running out of window area.

Some will overload cleanly so that the central portion can be examined safely, some will provide sufficient shift to enable the peaks to be examined safely—and by safely I mean without the 'scope adding its own distortion. This is not a satisfactory state of affairs, for amplitude measurements cannot be made, and anyway we cannot be sure that the waveform out of sight is behaving itself.

If we consider the customary 8cm × 10cm screen, we can arrive at a figure which will enable most frequently-met waveforms to be adequately 'scoped. If we assume that the highest amplitude signal we are most likely to meet will be no more than, say, 200 volts p-p, then an attenuator offering a maximum attenuation rate of 25V/cm will enable the signal to just fit the 8cm of screen. This assumes we are working single trace; if two such traces are involved, then immediately our screen area is halved, and the attenuation rate must be doubled to 50V/cm.

Many 'scopes have a variable fill-in control which will offer increased attenuation, but it is only calibrated at one end of its range; away from that it immediately becomes uncalibrated. So we have to resort to 'calibrating' it ourselves, either by means of a built-in signal—and this is usually 1V p-p or less—or against an external signal, a procedure which is not only time consuming, but may also introduce errors due to faulty equipment or technique. Far better to obtain a proper maximum range in the first place.

An alternative is to use a plug-in probe, and this is possibly a better solution, for it not only offers an attenuation that remains constant—typically ÷ 10—on all the 'scope attenuator settings, but perhaps more important for some applications, the input capacitance is considerably reduced.

The attenuators should be accurate to at least 3%, though a relaxation to around 5% may be permissible for non-critical measurements. This is not as patronising as it may appear at first sight, for to the tolerance of the attenuator we have to add the tolerance of the operator, and this is not always the most reliable factor!

### Fast Sweep Speeds

To make the most of an extended frequency response in the vertical axis, the 'scope must be provided with a timebase having sufficiently fast sweep speeds. There are two basic ways of deciding upon the fastest sweep required.

The first way is to decide how many 'cycles' of an event we want to spread over the entire screen width; a single cycle of a 1MHz input, for instance, will require a maximum sweep speed of 100nS/cm if required to occupy the full 10cm of screen, so that a full sweep is completed in 1$\mu$S, the reciprocal of which is, of course, 1MHz.

The second way must be used when risetimes are involved. Again, we must decide the amount of screen the risetime must occupy, and choose the timebase sweep speed accordingly. Reverting back to the point where we calculated the bandwidth required for a 50nS risetime, let us look at it again, this time in relation to timebase sweep speeds.

If the 50nS risetime must be expanded to the point where it occupies the entire screen, again a 10cm one, we will require a 5nS/cm sweep speed, a very fast speed indeed, and only provided in the top bracket 'scopes. So what do we do? Well, we can decide that we can tolerate a smaller stretch—this while less accurate is also more realistic.

Alternatively, we can utilise the timebase expansion provided on most 'scopes. This is usually × 10, though some cheaper 'scopes settle for × 5. They will give the effect of a timebase sweep speed × 5 or × 10 faster than it actually is, and will suffice for many measurements. A small penalty must be paid in the way of a degraded accuracy, usually about 2% to 3%. As long as the sweep is linear, it is immaterial which method is used, bearing in mind the slight loss in accuracy.

## Slow Sweep Speeds

At the other end of the sweep speed range, many 'scopes are provided with slow sweeps of around 0·5S/cm to 1S/cm, and with these the sweep will take 5 seconds or 10 seconds to traverse the 10cm screen. Now this sounds marvellously versatile, until you actually try to use such a slow sweep, particularly if it is slowed down even further by the inevitable variable control which has a range of around 2·5. The sweep will now be completed in no less a time than 12·5 seconds to 25 seconds.

No doubt the manufacturers will demand that I have my persistence of vision checked! To which I will reply that such slow sweeps are indeed useful if a *long persistence tube is fitted*! Photography is the only other alternative, but I suspect that people very seldom photograph very slow sweeps! So it all seems rather pointless providing such slow sweeps with a normal persistence tube, particularly when you come to reflect that the single timing capacitor has probably cost more than all the others put together.

## Delayed Timebases and Signal Delay

A delayed timebase can be a most valuable tool, but for what may be termed general purpose work, it is by no means essential and much good work can be done without its use. There are, clearly, applications where its use *is* essential, but these are also clearly of a specialised nature. Unless such work is part of the intended application, it is probably better to omit the delayed timebase and to put the money so saved to better use elsewhere.

Signal delay is quite another matter, and even modest amounts of delay can be most useful in enabling information to be retrieved that would otherwise be completely lost.

### Triggering Facilities

This is an area where strong men have been reduced to tears because inadequate triggering has made work quite impossible. Reliable and flexible triggering is an absolute *must*. Both the source and the polarity should be selectable, as should the precise point on the waveform where triggering takes place. For non-critical applications, or where the user feels a little lazy—and we all do from time to time—the triggering should be possible in the Auto mode.

The way in which these functions are presented varies from manufacturer to manufacturer, and indeed from 'scope to 'scope within a certain marque. Rotary switches, key switches, slide switches they all have a part to play, but a scheme which I find attractive is used in the Scopex range where a single knob controls not only polarity but slope, mechanical coupling being used to control the slope potentiometer and the polarity switch. Simplification without sacrifice of flexibility is well worth having.

### Number of Traces

Dual trace 'scopes cost more than single trace versions, for obvious reasons. The difference is not excessive if expressed as a percentage, and the dual trace 'scope is well worth having even if at first sight a single trace instrument appears to be adequate. Anyone who has become accustomed to dual trace working will verify that it can really be a most useful tool; it is surprising how often the dual traces are used.

### Ancillaries

Under this heading we will consider only the built-in calibrator that most 'scopes now possess. This may be nothing more than a mains frequency squarewave, but if it is accurately set-up, then it will enable the attenuator(s) to be individually set up for voltages outside the calibrated ranges, i.e. when the variable control is moved away from its calibrated position. The mains period of 20mS is accurately maintained, and so an accurate check of timebase speeds is also available.

An alternative is an oscillator—typically 1kHz—sometimes triggered from the mains frequency. The principle of useage is the same: an accurately determined output voltage and frequency to check the 'scope's vertical amplifier and timebase against.

A simple check for d.c. coupled 'scopes lacking an accurate calibrator is the Mercury cell, the voltage of which remains remarkably constant at 1·35 volts. If two *close tolerance* resistors of 330Ω and 1kΩ are placed in series across the cell, and the output taken across the 1kΩ resistor, the output is as near to 1 volts as practical considerations may require.

## Commercial 'Scopes

The top end of the market is firmly occupied by Marconi Instruments, Hewlett-Packard, and Tektronix, but not necessarily in that order. Somewhat lower down the scale—pricewise at least—we find Advance Electronics, Telequipment (a Tektronix subsidiary) Philips Electrical, Scopex and Grundig, again not necessarily in that order. Apologies to any company not mentioned but it is sometimes difficult to accurately 'place' a particular company in the Oscilloscopical Heirarchy, and so I may have inadvertently caused offence where none was meant.

I will confine myself to 'scopes of a general purpose nature (that most overworked of phrases) and leave the more exotic and specialised 'scopes to themselves. In fact 'general purpose' did at one time mean 'will do everything' and the unfortunate purchaser found himself with an oversize unit possessing features he would probably never use. Now, some semblance of sanity has reasserted itself, and the term 'general purpose' is applied to instruments covering from d.c. to around 25MHz to 40MHz, with input sensitivities of 5mV/cm and with timebases and triggering to match.

Ergonomically, 'scopes have improved enormously, while their physical bulk has shrunk, together with a great reduction in weight, not to mention power consumption. This has, in the main, been due to the adoption of semiconductor devices, and simple convection cooling can be used in place of the forced fan cooling of, perhaps, only a decade ago. Frequent recalibration has also been eliminated due to the stability of well-designed semiconductor circuits, and a periodical recalibration and/or check is now sufficient.

If cost is no consideration, then one can literally buy any 'scope that takes one's fancy, and here a three figure investment will be required. If you are in the same financial state as most of us, then no doubt the products of Messrs Advance, Scopex, and Telequipment will appeal to you.

I have not handled Telequipment equipment for several years, and since they resolutely declined to answer the several letters I wrote to them when preparing to commence writing this book, I cannot, quite clearly, comment on their current range. However, if past experience is anything to go by, their products should be viable within their price ranges.

Advance 'scopes, as I know from recent experience, are well designed ergonomically and physically—and this is more important than may at first sight be apparent. The specification, too, is well thought out, and the 'scopes in their entirety have been clearly designed by engineers for engineers.

My one small moan of both the OS250 and the OS1000A concerns the lack of *calibrated* attenuation above 20V/cm—see earlier remarks —and came about when I tried to use them on a capacitor discharge invertor where some 400 volts were floating about. This is probably a somewhat extreme case, and for the majority of users they will prove to be an excellent investment.

The OS250 could, for my particular needs—photographic records —benefit from the fitting of an illuminated graticule, but again this is not every one's requirement. At the time of writing, the prices of the OS250 and OS1000A at £175 and £255 respectively makes them an attractice proposition to the general purpose user.

An even cheaper pair of 'scopes from the same marque are the OS140 and OS240, single trace and dual trace respectively, with a smaller tube—4″—and a d.c. to 10MHz bandwidth. At £115 and £125 these seem to be the ideal instruments for training and educational work, amateurs, and our old friend the impoverished commercial user.

Scopex are a new firm to me, but their products appeal to me as being sensibly designed and priced, devoid of unnecessary frills, but containing the features necessary for quick, simple, and accurate work. Their 4D10 'scope is illustrated in Fig. 6.6.

### Second-hand 'Scopes

There are second-hand 'scopes to be had in all specification and price groups, and again finances largely dictate the final choice.

Fortunately for the second-hand purchaser, 'scopes are to a large extent 'tell-tale' instruments, inasmuch as it is soon possible for the knowledgeable purchaser to decide whether the one he is interested in is functioning more-or-less correctly.

The presence, or absence, of a trace will tell its own tale, and the built-in calibrating facilities usually incorporated will soon show whether the vertical amplifier(s) and timebase(s) are functioning correctly. With older 'scopes lacking calibrating facilities it is wise to try it out. A rough and ready check is to try the old finger routine to see if hum waveforms can be obtained.

A better idea, with d.c. coupled 'scopes, is to try the effect of a 1·5 volt cell on the vertical inputs and see how far the trace is deflected. A similar effect can be had with an a.c. coupled 'scope by rapidly making and breaking the cell contact. If no guarantee is offered, it is wise to try to arrange one, particularly if the vendor and/or 'scope is unknown. You may not succeed, but its worth a try!

## Kit 'Scopes

Inevitably, the name of Heathkit looms large when kits are in the offing. They offer a range of 'scopes encompassing a wide specification/price range. The cheapest one, and also the smallest and simplest, is the OS2, and the most comprehensive and expensive is the IO-104. Prices, at the time of writing, range from £38·90 to £201·95 for the OS2 and IO-104 if obtained as kits, while the assembled prices are necessarily higher. As with all Heathkit equipments, the manuals are models of excellence.

## Home Made 'Scopes

There was a time when there seemed to be one circuit or another published in the electronics periodicals suitable for home construction, mostly using surplus tubes of the VCR139—$3\frac{1}{2}''$—type. Whether the present dearth of designs is due to the unavailability of these tubes is debatable. Whatever the reason, there is no reason why the advanced amateur should not build his own—given a suitable circuit of course, unless he is advanced enough to design his own circuits.

My own home-made 'scope of 1964 vintage utilises a 6″ ex-radar VCR97 tube, has a bandwidth extending beyond 10MHz but not, regrettably, down to d.c. at a sensitivity of 100mV/cm. The attenuator follows my preferred steps of 1-3-10 and has a maximum attenuation of 30V/cm. The instrument is shown in Fig. 6.26.

## USING A 'SCOPE

Learning to use a 'scope is, to some extent, similar to learning shorthand; it is a new 'language', and perseverance and application are necessary to gain the experience that enables instant diagnosis to be made from the myriad waveforms that can be seen.

The amateur is at a considerable disadvantage here since he will have only a limited amount of equipment to practice with, and upon, and possibly no one to turn to for guidance. On the credit side, he does have an advantage in that his time is largely his own, and he *can* experiment.

Here it is as well to sound a serious warning. Experiments are fine, and the modern 'scope is virtually indestructible so you are most unlikely to damage it in any way. But you *can* damage yourself! All experiments should be treated seriously, and any involving a.c./d.c. equipment must be avoided like the plague, and this is the one exception that can very well damage both 'scope and user.

Television sets are particularly nasty since they are not only almost invariably a.c./d.c. operated but also operate at potentials (e.h.t.) that can certainly damage the best protected 'scope and cause bad burns to the operator into the bargain. This is assuming the worst, the best policy. If in doubt, don't. Its as simple as that! If you must, then do seek *properly qualified instruction*, and the little electrician round the corner is not your man, excellent as he may be in his own line.

### Instruction Books

With all new equipments, it is very worthwhile studying the instruction manual supplied, even if its only for a chuckle at Oriental English! With 'scopes, this is doubly important, and all the instruction manuals I have seen from British manufacturers have been excellent, those supplied by Marconi Instruments being even better, and are veritable mines of information; this is just as it should be, for the more complex the 'scope the more need for detailed information.

Heathkits are accompanied by excellent construction manuals, and these also include a short but useful summary on circuit operation, together with instructive notes on the use of the equipment concerned.

Even if you are *au fait* with the underlying principles, time studying the relevant instruction manual is indeed time well-spent. At worst, you will only have your knowledge confirmed; at best you may learn something new, some new application, a short cut. If you don't read the instruction manual, you'll never know. If you have a new second-hand 'scope, it is well worth trying to get hold of the instruction manual, if for no other reason than that of having the circuit.

## A.F. Amplifier Testing

This is probably the most common use for a 'scope amongst amateurs and those to whom, like myself, the a.f. reproducing process holds infinite interest. At the time I started work on this chapter, a friend complained of trouble with his Leak 30 stereo amplifier, and I decided that this was not an opportunity to be missed!

The test set-up was as shown in Fig. 5.14 except that as the amplifier was a stereo one the two inputs used—for simplicity, and since it was assumed that these would be nominally flat, the tuner inputs were used—were temporarily connected in parallel; also two heavy duty 8Ω load resistors were used. The various equipments used were those illustrated in Figs. 5.13, 3.12, 2.21, the 'scope being the Advance OS250. Y1 channel was used from time to time to monitor the input, most interestingly as it subsequently turned out.

## Reduced Power Output

The test started with an input signal at 1kHz, and the output is shown in Fig. 6.30 after it had been reduced to remove clipping. Even without the benefits of distortion measuring equipments it was clearly obvious that all was not well. The output from the l.h. channel was somewhat greater than that from the r.h. channel, though both were well down on the specification. No attempt was made to use the mV meter; instead the waveform was used to calculate the power output.

Taking the l.h. channel, represented by Y1, upper trace, the p-p amplitude was $\simeq$2·8cm, and as the attenuators were set to 5V/cm the total p-p voltage was 5 × 2·8 or 14 volts. Since $V_{rms} = 0·707 V_p$, the voltage corresponding to 14V p-p is 4·94, and this squared and divided by the 8Ω load resistance gives us the continuous power; in this case 3·05 watts of distorted power. The reader is left to work out for himself the power output from the r.h. channel form Y2!

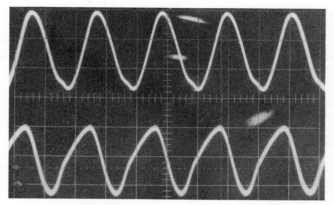

Fig. 6.30 Waveform obtained from Leak stereo amplifier just prior to clipping. (Y1 and Y2 set for 5V/cm deflection; timebase set at 0·5mS/cm).

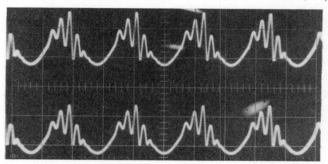

Fig. 6.31 Leak stereo amplifier. Effect of switching in 9kHz filter. (input frequency 10kHz).

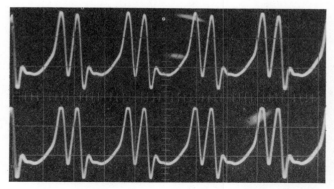

Fig. 6.32 As for Fig. 6.31, but with 4kHz filter switched in.

**Filter Ringing**

The Leak company were at one time famous for their *Varislope* filters, and so as a matter of curiosity the 9kHz filter was switched in, giving the almost unbelievable trace shown in Fig. 6.31. the input frequency having been increased to 10kHz. Reducing the filter roll-off to 4kHz produced the waveform shown in Fig. 6.32. Now, my friend uses a pair of KEF loudspeakers which though excellent quality-wise are somewhat inefficient, and this in conjunction with the use of the 9kHz filter was enough to make anyone without cloth ears complain!

This was indeed an intriguing amplifier, but the duties of authorship precluded my following my usual inquisitive investigations and delving into the 'innards' of the amplifier in search of the cause, and I had reluctantly to content myself by tweaking the power amplifier bias presets which improved matters considerably, powerwise, though the ringing was still present.

Not having the circuit of the Stereo 30 handy, I could only hazard a guess that the inductors used for the filter networks were ringing rather violently, most probably provoked by positive feedback from the power amplifiers via the supply lines. It is my practice to periodically check the input waveform, even though there is no real reason to suppose that anything is amiss, and this was one of the times that an idiosyncrasy proved useful, for the oscillogram of Fig. 6.33 was obtained.

The power output waveform is shown on the Y2 (lower) trace, while the input waveform is shown on the Y1 (upper) trace, and it is interesting to notice that the *input* waveform also shows ringing. The relative attenuator settings were 0·1V/cm for Y1 and 10V/cm for Y2. Switching the filter out of circuit stopped the ringing.

**Tone Controls**

The plotting of tone control circuit responses was detailed in Chapter 5 (Attenuators) so we can now examine alternative ways of checking tone control responses. The simplest way is by feeding in a squarewave and noting how it is affected by the various settings of the tone controls. If it emerges unscathed then either the tone controls are inoperative or else they are in a position where the overall response is truly flat, and this should, of course, correspond to the nominal 'flat' position of the controls.

A squarewave at a frequency of 1kHz was accordingly fed into the amplifier and the oscillogram of Fig. 6.34 was obtained. Y1

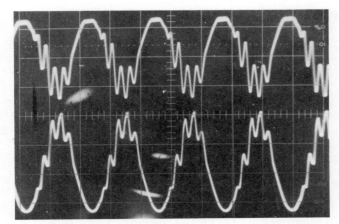

Fig. 6.33    Leak amplifier waveforms (Y1 input, 0·1V/cm ; Y2 output, 10V/cm ;
input frequency 10kHz. 9kHz filter switched into circuit).

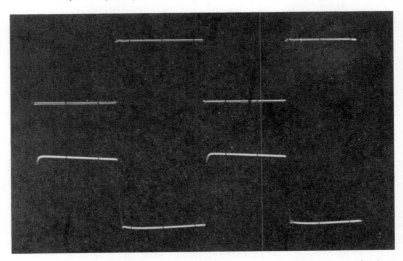

Fig. 6.34    Leak amplifier. (Y1 input, Y2 output with tone controls set for best
waveshape. Input frequency 1kHz).

shows the input waveform, and Y2 the output, after the controls
had been adjusted for the best waveform, not too far removed from
the nominal positions. The frequency was left unaltered, and the
effects of boost and cut of the treble and bass controls was tried.
Y1 of Fig. 6.35 shows the effect of maximum treble boost, whilst
Y2 shows the effect of maximum treblecut.

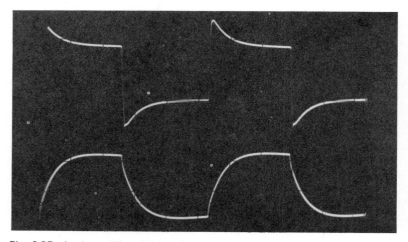

Fig. 6.35   Leak amplifier. (Y1, maximum treble boost; Y2, maximum treble cut. Input frequency 1kHz. Multiple exposure).

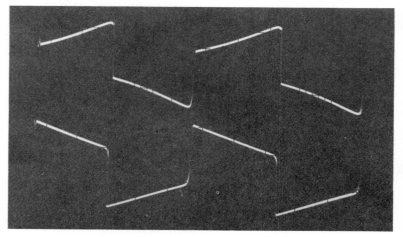

Fig. 6.36   Leak amplifier. (Y1, maximum bass boost; Y2, maximum bass cut. Input frequency 1kHz. Multiple exposure).

Fig. 6.36 shows, Y1, the effects of maximum bass boost, while Y2 shows the effects of maximum bass cut. These oscillograms reveal quite a useful amount of information to the practiced eye about the characteristics of the tone control circuits, and the beauty of it is that no plotting is involved, no frequency shifting, just a good squarewave, and a certain amount of practice!

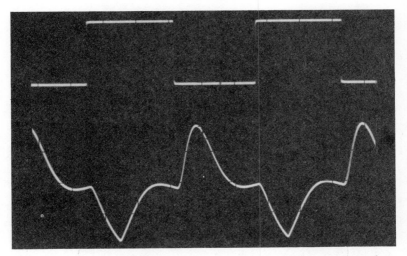

Fig. 6.37 Leak amplifier. (Y1, input frequency 10kHz; Y2, output waveform with maximum treble boost).

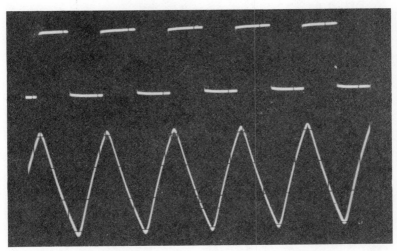

Fig. 6.38 Leak amplifier. (Y1, input frequency 10kHz; Y2, output waveform with maximum treble cut).

So far we have looked at oscillograms made at the nominal centre frequency of 1kHz. It is also very useful to examine the behaviour of the tone controls at the opposite ends of the bandwidth, and the frequencies used are frequently 100Hz and 10kHz. The input frequency was accordingly increased to 10kHz, and the treble control tuned to maximum boost; the resulting waveform is shown in Fig. 6.37, where Y1 is the input waveform and Y2 the output duly boosted. Fig. 6.38 shows the same input frequency, Y1, with the effects of maximum treble cut on Y2.

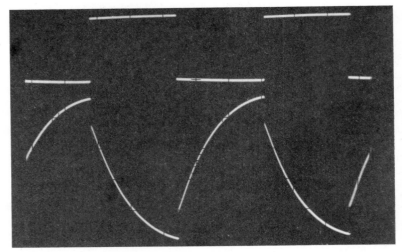

Fig. 6.39   Leak amplifier. (Y1, input frequency 100Hz; Y2, output waveform with maximum bass boost).

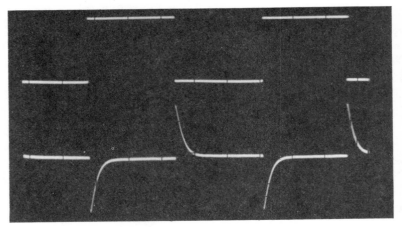

Fig. 6.40   Leak amplifier. (Y1, input frequency 100Hz; Y2, output waveform with maximum bass cut).

The treble control was duly returned to its previously determined flat position, and the effects of bass boost and cut were tried. Fig. 6.39 shows the 100Hz input frequency on Y1, while Y2 shows the effects of maximum bass boost. The effects of maximum bass cut are shown in Fig. 6.40, Y2, with Y1 again showing the 100Hz input frequency.

When checking tone controls, it is highly desirable to determine the actual 'flat' position, as this does not always correspond with the position marked on the amplifier, if in fact it is marked at all. Then, as each control is tried, it must be returned to its flat position before the other is tried; in this way, the effect of that control alone is determined. Also, as explained in Chapter 5, the increase in power output when the boost position of the tone controls is checked must be allowed for, otherwise amplifier overloading will occur and will totally vitiate the waveforms actually obtained.

Fig. 6.41 Equipment used for investigating the Leak amplifier, comprising Advance OS250 oscilloscope, home-built audio generator, dummy load resistors (behind oscilloscope), notebook and calculator used for rapidly determining power outputs, etc.

## Amplifier Damping

Another traditional use of the 'scope in conjunction with a square-wave is to check amplifiers for possible instability when feeding a simulated electrostatic loudspeaker. Few amplifiers are completely free from some overshoot under these circumstances, but the amount of ringing present should be minimal, or better still, absent. The simulation is effected by connecting a capacitor in parallel with the normal non-reactive load resistor, values from $0.1\mu F$ to $2\mu F$ being used. Fig. 6.42 shows the input waveform at 1kHz, (Y1) and the mild overshoot at the output with $2\mu F$ in parallel (Y2).

**Distortion**

The 'scope is an indispensible tool for the identifying of various *kinds* of distortion, though the actual *magnitude* must be measured by means of a Distortion Factor Meter, sometimes called a Harmonic Distortion Analyser, or by means of a Wave Analyser. For distortion measurements these instruments naturally complement each other. The 'scope on its own is of very limited use for assessing the amount of distortion present in any sinusoidal waveform, and it is doubtful if many users could say with any degree of certainty whether a displayed signal contained 2 or 3% of distortion or only 0.001%.

**Bias Adjustment**

Fig. 6.43 shows the effect of power amplifier bias maladjustment. The input signal (Y1) is to all practical intents distortion free. The power output (Y2) certainly is not, as evidenced by the clipping of the positive peak, and such clipping would have an audible —and unpleasant—effect on the knowledgeable ear. Provided there is nothing radically wrong with the amplifier, it should be possible to readjust the bias presets to obtain symmetrical clipping when over-driven, and this should also increase the power output somewhat.

In this little section of this chapter it has been possible to show just a very few of the uses of the 'scope. The more mundane, or well-known, have been deliberately omitted, as have those of a more specialised nature. There are numerous books devoted solely to the use of the 'scope, and the reader of this one is urged to read as many books as he can get hold of, be they bought or borrowed. There will, inevitably, be some small disagreement between them, but the important thing is that what one book leaves out another will deal with. This is, remember, a new language, shorthand if you like, and only application and practice will bring about its mastery.

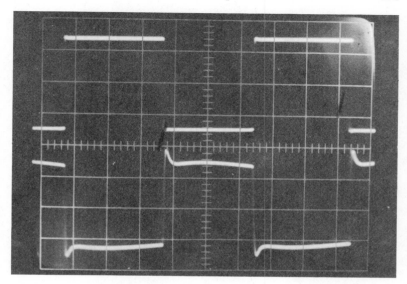

Fig. 6.42 Input waveform at 1kHz on Y1. Y2 shows slight overshoot from power amplifier loaded with $8\,\Omega$ resistor and $2\mu$F capacitor to simulate electrostatic loudspeaker.

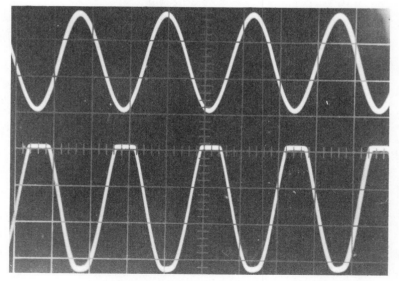

Fig. 6.43 Incorrect bias level in power output stage. Y1, input 100mV r.m.s.; Y2, output 22·4V p-p across $8\,\Omega$.

# RECORDING FROM THE 'SCOPE

There are occasions when it is necessary to make a record of the waveform displayed on the 'scope. If the trace is a stable one, and in the absence of more advanced facilities, it is quite possible to make a permanent facsimile by placing a piece of transparent, or semi-transparent material over the screen and then carefully tracing out, in pencil or Chinagraph (wax pencil) as the material demands, the displayed waveform. The result will depend upon the care and skill exercised by the operator, and, as with all such operations, practice will make perfect, even to the extent of enabling quite slow sweeps to be copied exactly.

Where a large number of traces have to be recorded, the tracing operation can become onerous and time consuming; also in common with many repetitive operations boredom or carelessness may set in, to the detriment of the work. It is therefore worth exploring alternative methods of recording.

## Photographic Recording

The most used method for obtaining numerous traces, or copies of traces, is the photographic one. A number of specialised systems —cameras and films—are available, and details of these can be obtained from the respective suppliers. We, being either impoverished or very occasional photographers of c.r.t.'s must needs look at other methods!

There is a major difference between what may be termed normal photography and the photography of c.r.t. displays. The normal photograph—except in the case of high-key or low-key subjects—must contain, in theory at least, the full range of tones from deepest black to whitest white. The oscillogram need contain only two: the c.r.t. trace, which on the negative should be absolutely black, and the screen itself which should reproduce as clear gelatin. To this we may need to another tone, that of the graticule, which will most probably reproduce in some shade of grey.

The constitution of the normal photograph need not concern us here; the oscillogram most certainly does. The waveform on the c.r.t. is built up of a succession of sweeps of a single spot of light traversing the tube, and the final density is a compromise between the number of sweeps, the tube e.h.t. and the sweep speed, and will be dimmest when the highest sweep speeds are used, together with X expansion.

Fig. 6.44   Advance OS140 and OS240 oscilloscopes, low-cost 10MHz single and dual trace instruments.

The resulting negative is a line negative, i.e. is all black or all white (clear) and therefore errors in exposure and development that would be intolerable in normal photography are acceptable, and will yield a useable print. Exposure determination, as such, is totally impossible, and empirical or trial-and-error methods have to be used. Most people end up evolving their own technique, but for what it is worth a few notes may help the total beginner.

All my own oscillograms are photographed on to Ilford FP4, a film I have used ever since it superceded FP3, and this is developed in Patterson *Acutol*. A more contrasty film/developer combination would be better still, but for the few oscillograms I make in a year I prefer to use a combination I know well. A concession is to extend development by 50%.

The camera used is a Microcord I have had since they were fashionable, in conjunction with a close-up lens. The parallax correcting lens is not quite accurate enough for my liking, and so I have made a slide which allows the complete camera to be slid up and down by the distance between the taking and viewing lenses. The close-up lens is changed between taking and focusing lenses, as appropriate; the only problem is that I sometimes forget to alter either the slide or the lens! An exposure of f8 @ $\frac{1}{2}$ second suits my work.

Having said that, it must be pointed out that this was an exposure that was determined after several rolls of films had been exposed and developed, and some of the more indifferent oscillograms had perforce to be included, simply because the 'scopes used were on loan for a limited period only, and the opportunity of repeating the oscillograms did not present itself.

Some of the oscillograms were made by means of multiple exposures, a useful and film-saving scheme where it is not essential to have both traces photographed simultaneously. Multiple exposures are made very simply by positioning the trace where required, making an exposure, moving the trace, and making another exposure. A little care is required in positioning the traces, and it is wise to allow a little time to elapse between exposures so that the phosphor has time for any excitation afterglow to decay. By this means I have made as many as three exposures on a single negative (Fig. 6.13) and this is clearly a valuable facility, not least for authors.

### Close-up Lenses

Close-up lenses enable almost any camera to be used, and can be obtained in various 'strengths'; this is dependent on the focal length. With fixed-focal length cameras, the camera-to-subject distance is fixed, and is determined by the focal length of the close-up lens.

Variable focus cameras can be used between distances defined by the normal focusing range of the camera, and by the focal length of the close-up lens. These are normally rated in dioptres, which is the reciprocal of focal length in metres, and can be obtained in dioptre ratings between $+1$ to $+5$. A $+3$ dioptre lens, the most used rating, will enable a camera with a focusing travel from infinity to 39″ to be used between 13″ and 10″ from the subject.

The camera must be firmly mounted on a tripod or other support, facing the 'scope, and as perpendicular to the screen as possible. After very careful focusing, the room lights must be extinguished, otherwise reflections will mar the photographs obtained. Some afterglow can be noticed from a screen if the light is extinguished, but I have never had any photographic problems from this effect. The exposure can now be made, preferably by a cable release; alternatively the self-timer can be used.

### Development

It is highly desirable that a single film is devoted to the business of securing oscillograms, so that it can receive proper—in our case extended—development. The first film will almost certainly prove unsatisfactory, and this is to be expected, for after all this is our first venture into the oscillogram business. If the first film is satisfactory, we possess either a great measure of luck, or else previous experience.

Depending on the appearance of the negatives, and these *must* be treated as line negatives, and not as continuous tone negatives, either the exposure time, or the development time, or both may require alteration. The *screen* area should be completely clear, and this will then appear black on the print. The trace should appear in stark contrast, without any diffusion or streaking. Assuming the camera was carefully and accurately focused, the streaking will most probably be caused by over exposure. A correctly exposed and developed trace will print as pure white. The graticule should appear either stark black (on the negative) or as an intermediate tone, and will then appear as pure white or as a light grey on the print.

A possible source of trouble is the graticule illumination. This is normally orange, while the trace will be green, blue-green, or blue. Some difficulty may be experienced in balancing the relative brilliance of the trace and the graticule, and since the colour balance of the eye is not quite the same as the colour balance of the film some experiments may be necessary in arriving at a stisfactory balance as seen on the photographic print.

### Single Shot Work

For single shot work, the shutter can either be synchronised to the trigger for the timebase, or if this is impracticable, it can be left on 'time' or on 'brief' until the sweep is completed, when it can be closed. The same technique can be used when excessively long sweeps are involved.

A problem peculiar to single shot and slow sweep speed work is that of insufficient intensity, since these lack the build-up of intensity provided by recurrent sweeps, and therefore a wide aperture lens is required. True, the camera shutter can be left open indefinitely to obtain the effect of multiple sweeps with *repeatable* single shot phenomena, more so with recurrent slow sweeps, but here we are faced with the uncertainty of knowing just how accurately the successive sweeps overlap.

### The Camera

To close, it must be mentioned that the ideal camera, viewing-wise, is the single lens reflex. The majority of these are fitted with focal plane shutters, and a possible cause of trouble is that all, or part, of the waveform may be missing on the negative if the shutter speed is similar to, or faster than, the sweep speed. This is due to the operation of the focal plane shutter where exposure variation is effected—shutter-wise—by altering the width of the slit between the two blinds forming the shutter proper, the speed of the blinds being almost constant.

It is therefore quite possible for the shutter to have completed its operation before the sweep, resulting in the missing part on the negative; just to make matters more interesting (worse?) the effect depends on the relative directions of shutter and sweep! The cure is simply to ensure that the shutter speed is considerably longer than the sweep speed.

### Closing Comments

In this book it has been possible to cover just some of the test instruments that are available, and it is hoped that the reader has gained not only edification but also pleasure from reading this addition to the Fountain Press technical books. Those readers requiring further enlightenment can be recommended to companion volumes, such as John Earl's *Audio Technician's Bench Manual* and H. W. Hellyer's *Radio Technician's Bench Manual*, both of which cover the 'using' side of electronic test instruments, the titles reflecting the subject content. Both books are eminently 'readable'.

For further coverage of the oscilloscope, readers are referred to *The Oscillosope in Use*, by Ian R. Sinclair, at the time of writing in preparation for publication by Fountain Press.

Beyond these books are many dealing with specific instruments, and a browse amongst the technical books in any reasonably comprehensive library will bring at least one or two suitable books to light. As a general purpose reference book, Scroggie's Radio and Electronic Laboratory Handbook is justly famous, and though somewhat expensive is worth every penny.

To close on a personal note, I have over the years developed the philosophy that it is better to buy a book than borrow it, for it is the inevitable quirk of fate that reference to a borrowed book almost invariably becomes necessary *after* it has been returned!

# INDEX

197